"Chalcie,  Chatain f and foreve

Chalcie look tightened again around her wrist. There escape.

"I do."

"Jordan, do you take Chalcedony Kent for your wife?"

"I do," he said as the clock began to strike the first note of midnight.

Jordan leaned down and kissed Chalcie. She tasted sweet, and for just a moment he allowed himself to think that life with her could be equally as sweet, if she'd give him a chance to show her they might fall in love, after all.

Ann Pope is a full-time author who, despite her lack of interest in history as a student, enjoys the subject today. Her reading and the many locales in which she has lived through the years inspired her to begin writing historical romances. In her free time, Ann keeps herself busy rescuing animals, quilting and playing the bagpipe. At present, she lives with her husband in California.

GOLD FEVER

Ann Pope

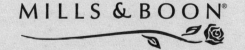

MILLS & BOON®

First published in Great Britain 1999
Harlequin Mills & Boon Limited,
Eton House, 18-24 Paradise Road, Richmond, Surrey TW9 1SR

© Ann Zavala 1991

ISBN 0 263 81840 3

Set in Times Roman 10½ on 11 pt.
04-9911-91360

Printed and bound in Spain
by Litografia Rosés S.A., Barcelona

Chapter One

Sonora, California, 1849

"Chalcie, there's a pack train coming in, and it's stopped right outside Jordan's place," Juanita, the bartender, said as she lifted the calico curtain and ducked inside the tiny three-sided room that served as her boss's bedroom, workroom and office. The braying of the mules from the pack train almost drowned out the sounds of the bustling gold mine camp of Sonora.

Juanita sighed in exasperation as she looked at Chalcedony. She was wearing that damned pink dress again. She knew that her boss had all kinds of gold coming in from the various Kent enterprises scattered around town, so why did she insist on wearing the one dress that made her hair look like carrot curls and every freckle on her face stand out against her tan. Chalcie didn't look good, Juanita decided. Her eyes were dark with fatigue brought on by trying to devise more ways to bring in more gold, and she wondered if Chalcie could be satisfied with less than owning everything in town.

"Why do you do this to yourself?" Juanita demanded.

"The only person in all of Sonora who could challenge you is Jordan de Chatain, and even he isn't as rich or as smart as you. Why don't you concentrate on finding a proper husband for yourself?"

Chalcedony Kent closed the green leather ledger that recorded the day's business. She ignored Juanita's comments. Her friend might think she was ready for romance and marriage, but Chalcie knew better; she'd rather concentrate on business than love.

"A pack train stopping at Jordan's? Lucky him, at least he's got someone reliable to send down to Stockton to bring whiskey and flour for the bars," Chalcie said. She was still furious with her father. The man simply had no head for business! The latest wrong decision he'd made had been to send Houlihan down to Stockton for supplies. "I'll bet Houlihan has already drunk up every cent that we gave him, and he's probably sold the mules, too. And here we are, with winter not that far away. All that money and we're not going to see a pound of flour out of it!"

"Your father doesn't have the best sense in choosing men, does he?" Juanita sympathized.

"He has never in his whole life chosen a partner or a worker who was worth anything," Chalcie answered truthfully. About the only way her father could have made matters worse would have been to choose Jordan de Chatain as his partner and then let the man undercut everything that Chalcie had worked for. She was glad her father had never thought of Jordan as a potential partner, because it would have spelled the end of the Kent enterprises. Jordan would stop at nothing to bring the men into the Dry Gulch Saloon. He had wooed away her best cook to make the oyster stew that he served every night. He'd brought in fancy drapes and a gilt-edged mirror, and installed a long mahogany bar. Some of the miners even said there were pictures in the back room that no lady should know about, much less ever see. All of it was de Chatain's handiwork and all of it had cut into her profits.

Chalcie didn't hold with fancy frills in the bar. She was willing to serve fresh bread and rolls and to make certain that the saloon's packed dirt floors were swept once a day. The girls who worked in the C. K. Saloon were pretty and the drinks weren't cut too much. She figured that men came to a bar to drink, not to be served good food or look at a gold-wrapped mirror. Being poor had left its mark on her way of doing business. Chalcie was too cautious to throw money away on something that might not pay back the investment.

Still she worried. What was de Chatain up to now? Damn the man! It would have been so much easier to fight him if she didn't find him both interesting and attractive. No one would ever have guessed that she saw him as anything other than an enemy. There had been times, though, when no one was watching, that she had stood in the shadows and stared at him. She watched him as he moved down the street, lithe, darkly handsome, wearing his fine clothes.

Chalcie had never told anyone—even Juanita—about her weakness for Mr. de Chatain, for it could have been used against her. Instead, she focused on business, and the business at the moment was the news about the pack train.

"The mules were being led down the alleyway between the Dry Gulch and Brad McClatchy's land, and I thought you'd like to take a look, just in case," Juanita said. She didn't want Chalcedony to be taken by surprise if Jordan was planning something new to draw in a crowd to the Dry Gulch.

Chalcie looked at Juanita in tacit agreement.

"I'll go set things up in the bar so we're ready for the first miners coming back from the diggin's, and then I'll join you out back. You keep an eye on Jordan and see what surprises he's got in store for us," Juanita said as they left the small room.

Chalcie nodded, already concentrating on the sound of the clink and rattle and bray of the pack train as the animals were led behind the Dry Gulch Saloon. She swore silently as she watched the burros plod through the dust.

She was furious with the man. Why couldn't he just take his profits and be content with them? She wanted to hit something. Instead, she gathered the material from her skirt into her fists, making creases in her work-worn pink calico dress. It wasn't fair that Jordan got his supplies in while she was still waiting for her own. If her father hadn't trusted Houlihan, everything would have been fine, but the man James Kent had chosen to go to Stockton was a drunken no-good thief.

She forced herself to relax. She could think better when she wasn't working in a blind fury. Her hands released the hated pink calico, the color her father had picked that made her red hair look like overripe vegetables. His sense of color was as bad as his sense of friendship.

Chalcedony decided that she'd just have to go back there and find out for herself what Jordan de Chatain was planning this time—so she could plan retaliation.

"I've got a surprise for you, Mr. de Chatain. This time I'm going to fight back. You're not going to bring in another gilt mirror or mahogany bar or more pretty ladies to ruin my business...." As Chalcie rounded the corner she thumped nose first into Jordan de Chatain's firmly muscled chest.

"Ouch—oh, damn it!" Chalcie swore, tears springing to her eyes. She wavered as the pain made everything else disappear. She couldn't see, she couldn't think, she couldn't even talk as the blood began to spurt from her nose.

"What the hell...?" Jordan's voice boomed in surprise as he was hit full in the chest by Chalcie. Instinctively he reached out to grab her before she could fall.

Chalcie swayed against his hands. She could already feel the bruising and swelling that was starting underneath her eyes and in the soft tissue of her nose. She wiped at her eyes, trying to see Jordan, and suddenly began to lose her balance again.

"Hey, watch out!" Jordan tightened his hand around her waist, very much aware that her skin was warm beneath the thin calico. She didn't look very pretty at the moment, but he was very aware that underneath the faded dress there was a wonderfully filled-out woman's body. Besides, he'd always had a real weakness for pretty blue eyes and golden-red hair. If she hadn't been his most serious competition, he might have made an effort to court her long ago. At the moment, the blood from her nose tended to make him by-pass his usual enjoyment of the compact and very interesting female form for concerns about her welfare.

Chalcie was aware through the pain that Jordan de Chatain was holding her close against his chest and that he was just as warm and strong as she had ever thought he would be. She tried to ask him to let her go, but she couldn't quite force the words out. Instead she snuffled. She also tried to squirm out of his grasp, even though she couldn't see clearly.

"Stop flailing around. You're still not steady on your feet, and if I let you go, you'd fall right there in that mass of mule dung," Jordan chided. He wasn't in any hurry to put her down. He'd never had Chalcedony Kent at his mercy before, and he was rather enjoying the feeling.

Jordan moved away a few feet from the offending pile of manure and gently set Chalcie back on the ground. He bent forward to examine the damage, still steadying her with his hand on her arm.

"I'm sorry, really, I am." He shook his head in pity. "It looks pretty bad. One black eye for certain. Maybe both."

He touched her lightly on the nose, assessing the damage. "I never intended to hurt you. If I'd known you were going to come charging around the corner, I wouldn't have been standing there. I've never liked being run over by women, anyway."

The pain finally began to subside, and Chalcie's temper was rising. She felt stupid for having run into him, and she felt even more ridiculous for liking the feel of his hands around her waist and his fingers on her face when he checked her bruised nose.

"What were you doing blocking my way? How dare you just stand there and fill up the whole passageway!" Chalcie shot back. She knew she was being ridiculous, she should have rounded the corner more slowly, but she couldn't help herself. Her nose hurt, the whole front of her only dress was sticky with blood, and it was all because Jordan had such a hard chest.

Jordan just smiled, making Chalcie even more furious.

"Buck, bring me a towel dipped in water," Jordan ordered one of the men who had been standing behind him when Chalcie ran into his chest.

"But—"

"Do it now," Jordan growled.

Buck was back almost immediately with the towel.

"Here, let's get some of the blood cleaned off." Jordan reached out with the edge of the towel and cleaned Chalcie's face.

"I really am sorry," Jordan apologized again as he folded the towel and handed it back to Buck. He looked at the swelling beneath her eyes again and frowned. If it had happened to any other woman, he would have invited her to come inside and rest in his office behind the bar. He could have given her the best brandy the house could offer as a painkiller, and a free dinner whipped up by Chalcie's ex-cook. Unfortunately, he didn't think Chalcie would look kindly on the invitation.

Chalcie drew a deep breath, trying to steady herself. If she hadn't been blinded by the pain of her poor bashed nose, she'd never have allowed Jordan de Chatain to touch her, no matter how gentle he was. He was her enemy, not a man who was courting her. And her own personal attraction to him wasn't even worth thinking about. She didn't have time for such nonsense.

"I'm fine, thank you," Chalcie said stiffly. She pushed his hand away. "I can manage now."

The film of tears had cleared and she could finally see Jordan. She wished for the hundredth time that he wasn't quite so good-looking. And hard, she added. His chest was hard as a rock. It was obvious from her brief but very close encounter that there wasn't an ounce of fat on his six-foot-plus frame. As usual, his dark hair looked slightly mussed, as if he'd just done some hard physical work. His black eyes gleamed with amusement, and there was the barest beginning of a smile at the corners of his mouth. In fact, it looked like he was about to start laughing at her.

"Since you came running back here in such an all-fired hurry, let me guess what you're doing. It probably has something to do with what the pack mules are carrying, right?" Jordan asked. He was glad to change the subject. He was also delighted at finding Chalcie in a hurry to snoop around the pack train. That meant she was worried about what he'd do next to draw business away from her establishment.

Jordan whipped a bright red silk kerchief from the pocket of the work shirt that he had changed into and brushed off the dust from a cedar stump that had been left when the two saloons and the storage shacks were being built. Jordan offered the stump to her as if it were the finest chair in a proper parlor.

"Here, have a seat where you can watch every single bundle and box that is unloaded. But you're going to get mighty tired of counting barrels of flour and kegs of whiskey."

His black eyes gleamed with devilish delight at being able to poke fun at his chief rival. He enjoyed making Chalcie squirm. Part of the pleasure came from trying to break through her prickly exterior to find out if there was any sense of fun lurking underneath the toughness. Long ago he had decided that her seriousness was the reason she didn't make the profits that she could have with her businesses. She didn't have a playful bone in her body, and for that he blamed that no-good father of hers, James Kent.

However, that family trouble wasn't any of his business, and he intended to keep it that way, even if she was one of the more intriguing and attractive women in the gold country.

"Please, spend all day out here if you want. I'll even supply you with a parasol if you need one, to protect your delicate skin." He stopped for a moment and smiled tenderly at her. "Did you know, with your poor battered nose, black eye and hair down in braids, you look like an urchin who's had a rough day!"

"I look like your worst enemy, that's who I look like," Chalcie said through gritted teeth. He had no right to taunt her about being as brown as a heathen and so freckled that her own grandmother wouldn't recognize her. She didn't have the time or the energy to bother with protecting herself from the California sun. Chalcie pulled herself up to her full height, which was still barely level with Jordan's impressive shoulders, and glared at him, her blue eyes blazing. She was angry enough that her usually generous lips had thinned to a straight line.

"And I'm not interested in your old pack train. I was going out to take inventory," Chalcie stated. "I didn't even know you were back here."

Jordan smiled at her. It was obvious he didn't believe her.

Chalcie continued. "You can bring in whatever you want and I don't care. It doesn't bother me at all." She brushed past him and pulled out the keys for her storeroom from the pocket of her dress. Chalcie leaned over, pulling the heavy brass lock toward her, checking to make certain that no one had been trying to break into the storehouse and help themselves.

"Damn," Jordan said, the smile still evident in his voice as he watched the play of material across her rounded bottom.

"What did you say?" Chalcie whirled to face him again.

"Nothing, sorry, I didn't say a thing," Jordan said, raising his hands. He'd never have been fool enough to admit that the outline of Chalcie's body beneath the worn cotton dress was delectable. She'd have attacked him on the spot. Jordan had no doubt that there was a small gun or a very sharp knife concealed somewhere in that dress, and he knew Chalcie would think nothing of using it on him. Indeed, if she could blast him into the next world, he had no doubt that she would be quite satisfied with the results. She would be able to buy all of Sonora without the challenge of Jordan de Chatain to stop her avaricious real estate raids.

But Jordan knew something Chalcie didn't. He knew that no matter how long she waited, she wouldn't see the three small boxes that had already been unloaded, nor would she meet the lady who was going to bring in crowds to the bar later that evening, after she had a chance to set up her new and wonderful music box contraption inside the Dry Gulch Saloon.

"Chalcie, are things all right back here? What about the inventory…" Juanita stopped in midsentence and stared at her friend. Chalcie was a mess. Her eyes were swollen and her nose was bruised.

"Oh, my God," Juanita whispered. She whipped around, ready to beat Jordan to a pulp.

Jordan raised his hands and retreated. "It isn't as bad as it looks. I didn't do anything, honestly. She ran into me." Jordan was embarrassed by the look Juanita shot him. "You know me, Juanita. You know I'd never deliberately hurt a woman!" He looked at Juanita's black eyes and the expression on her small brown face and hoped that she knew him well enough to know he was telling the truth.

Chalcie waved away Juanita's concern. "Don't even bother to ask," Chalcie sighed. "Let's get into the storeroom and take inventory, since my supplies seem to be caught somewhere between Stockton and Sonora."

She ignored the smile of triumph that spread slowly across Jordan's handsome face. He knew perfectly well that she was going to be staying close by, in her shed, and watching everything that was being unloaded off the pack train. The man was impossible!

Two hours later Chalcie and Juanita knew every barrel, bottle and bag in their own storeroom and almost as much about what went into Jordan's storage area. They had counted and sorted and cleaned and spied. Chalcie had cobwebs stuck in her hair, and Juanita had ripped her skirt on a nail that had been left by the men who put the shed together.

"Chalcie, this is crazy." Juanita finally flung herself down on one of the barrels and fanned her face. Dust motes danced in the sunshine that streamed through the door of the shack. Inside the wooden walls, the temperature had soared to over a hundred, and Juanita was ready to give up. Her brown face was streaked with perspiration.

"All we've seen come off those mules is flour and sugar and whiskey, and about a hundred tins of oysters for their stew. There isn't anything else there!"

"Yes there is. I know there is. He's planning something to cut into our business!" Chalcie insisted.

"Well, if he is, there isn't anything you can do about it."

"I have to fight. I'm not letting him just walk away with the money. Look what happened when I sat back and ignored him while he built the fourth wall for his bar, so that he was using real doors instead of a calico curtain. And then he took my cook, and now the Dry Gulch Saloon serves oyster stew and I have to make do with what that Chinese guy can make. This time I'm going to beat him at his own game."

"How?" Juanita challenged her.

"I'll think of something, and it won't include spending money on fripperies, either," Chalcie said.

The last two words were punctuated by the sound of some kind of music that neither of them had ever heard before from next door.

Chalcie slammed her hand against the wall of the shed, making it rock forward almost to the point of collapse.

"There, you see, he's up to something and we got back here too late to find out what it was. Damn, if I'd only been faster on my feet, I might have been able to counterattack tonight and spoil his surprise."

Chalcie wiped her hands on her skirt and blew wisps of hair out of her face. She might have lost this round, but she hadn't lost the battle. Someday, somehow, she was going to get the edge on Jordan de Chatain, and when she did, she'd wipe him out.

The strange music kept up during the afternoon and into the evening. By the time the miners started to drift back in from their digs, everyone knew that Jordan was concocting something big in the Dry Gulch Saloon, and the speculation had reached a fever pitch around the street.

Finally, almost at midnight, the first reports came in, and Chalcie and Juanita watched in disbelief as the men surged out of their bar and toward the Dry Gulch Saloon.

"He's got an Egyptian lady doing some kind of dance with veils and a music box."

"He's charging a pinch of gold to go in and look at her."

"Whatever it is, I'll pay it...."

"Is she going to stay here, do you think? Is she married?"

The questions swirled around Chalcie.

"And I hear that today he actually got a cat for himself. Paid a hundred dollars for it and another hundred to have it brought to Sonora. He's keeping it at home. Said he needed an office cat to watch over his books."

Chalcie could have dismissed the threat of the dancer and the new music. She could always counter that by bringing in a new singer or two, imported straight from the halls in San Francisco. One way or another, the men would come back to the C. K. Saloon. But the cat was another thing entirely.

Chalcie had never thought she would leave her grandmother's home in Boston by any other means than marriage. Then, one day when she was ten years old, her father had suddenly reappeared on the doorstep and announced that he wanted to take Chalcie out for a ride in the park. Her grandparents had been reluctant but had finally agreed. It was the last time that Chalcie had seen either her grandparents or the kittens that she had rescued that spring.

Chalcie's grandmother had surprised her by accepting the kittens and even going so far as to provide a special milk and showing her how to feed the babies with a cloth that they could suck on. The orange fluffs had grown into two beautiful cats, one with fur that closely matched Chalcie's own hair in color.

Chalcie could talk of nothing else but her cats when she ran down the steps to her father's waiting carriage. James Kent had lied, though. He and Chalcie had never returned to the house. They had headed out of Boston, running to Texas, where her father was certain that his in-laws would never find him or his daughter.

Kent, the adventurer, had stolen Chalcie, never realizing that she would have gladly stayed with her grandmother. Now, ten years later, Chalcie felt the unbearable pain of the loss again.

"Chalcie, what's wrong?"

Juanita saw the dead white of Chalcie's skin, even under the tan. Her friend was barely breathing. She had her hands clasped in front of her as if she were trying to hold on to something invisible.

"Did your nose suddenly start hurting? I didn't expect it to cause you any trouble tonight—"

"No, nothing like that." Chalcie couldn't tell her friend about the memories that had been reawakened or she'd start crying. And this was no time for tears. "If you can handle the crowds, I think I'll go out for a walk."

She had to see the cat. Chalcie knew that she was being foolish. She knew that if she was caught, her reputation would be in tatters. But the longing was so intense that she could think of nothing else.

Besides, there wasn't any reason for Jordan ever to know. Chalcie changed into a green shirt and dark cotton trousers. A heavy pair of miner's boots and a scarf around her neck completed the disguise that she needed. A dark brown leather hat made her red hair disappear, and she was ready for the foray into the enemy camp.

Jordan's bar was still filled with men, though the crowd had thinned considerably from the early evening rush. Chalcie watched through the open doors and windows until she caught sight of Jordan. He was in the middle of the crowd and it didn't look as if he was going anywhere soon. She would be safe.

Chalcie worked her way through the throng of miners toward the edge of town. She'd seen Jordan's house from a distance but had never been invited inside. She knew, however, that it was the grandest house in the year-old settlement at Sonora. It actually had two rooms and a porch and a stove for heating and cooking.

"That's the difference between Jordan and me," Chalcie muttered. "He invests in things, and I invest in land. I can live in a room that only has a calico wall, because I know that I've still got the gold in my pocket instead of invested in fir and cedar that will burn in the next fire."

Jordan, of course, also didn't have a father like James Kent to contend with, she thought.

The house was dark and silent as Chalcie approached it. She stepped up on the back porch and heard the washbasin rattle. From inside there was a slight sound and a soft "meow."

If the cat hadn't meowed, Chalcie thought later, she never would have gone into the house. She would have realized that she was crazy and turned around and gone back home.

Instead, she opened the door and hurried inside. She found a candle in the box hanging on the wall beside the door and lighted it with a match. Then she looked for the cat.

The animal wasn't in sight, and she searched through the kitchen and into a combination bedroom and office. The green ledgers from all of Jordan's businesses were laid neatly to one side of the pine-plank desk. On the other side, there were papers, letters and what seemed to be several plans for future expansion. She studiously avoided looking at them. She wasn't here to snoop; she was here to look at the cat.

"Meow."

Chalcie jumped and looked down, almost at her feet. A small orange-and-white female rubbed against the rough canvas of her pants. She stared straight up at Chalcie and then meowed again.

Chalcie bent down and touched the soft fur. She rubbed the area behind the cat's ears and was rewarded by a trembling purr.

She was unaware of anything else in the room. The sound of the men in town quieted, the smell from the cedars outside and the dust that rose in the air faded. Nothing mattered but the feel of the cat beneath her hands and the memories that came flooding back. If only she knew for certain what had happened after her father had stolen her away that Sunday afternoon. Had her grandparents searched for her and then given up, never knowing where she had gone?

She couldn't count the times she had tried to write a letter to her grandmother, only to have her father discover it and rip the pages into tiny pieces. She finally managed to send a letter secretly. She had waited for months, hoping that her grandmother would write and she would know, finally, what had transpired in Boston after all these years. But there had been no answer, at least not one she ever received.

Tears began to run down her face, but she was oblivious to them. That was the way that Jordan found her ten minutes later, sitting on the log that served as a stool in front of his desk. The glorious fall of red hair had worked its way loose from beneath the hat, and her body was outlined underneath the shirt as she held the cat, stroking it softly.

"May I guess that you've looked through enough of my books to know just how my finances are set up and what profits I've been enjoying? Or were you more interested in my plans for the next few months?" Jordan's voice cut through her memories and shocked Chalcie back into the present.

Chalcie screamed and dropped the cat, which promptly scuttled underneath the bed. Chalcie's heart was in her mouth, and she almost fainted from the fright. Suddenly her nose began to throb again, and she had the awful feeling that another nosebleed was going to start from the sheer shock of hearing Jordan's voice.

She stood up, her hands to her face in utter mortification. She had never intended to be caught like this!

"I didn't look, I wouldn't... I didn't come here to snoop—" she started to explain, but he cut her off angrily.

"I've known for a long time that you resented my money-making proficiency. I knew that you were jealous of the ways I manage to bring the business into the Dry Gulch and out of the C.K., but I never thought that you were the kind of person who would stoop to breaking into my office."

"But I wouldn't—"

"Yes, you would. I didn't invite you here, did I?"

Chalcie looked down at her feet. What could she say? "No," she answered, her voice low and miserable.

"And you did come into this house when I wasn't here, didn't you?"

"Yes."

"And you came only to snoop around and inspect my books, didn't you? Because there isn't another reason in

the world that you should be here.'' Jordan put his hands
on his hips, challenging her with his irrefutable logic.

Breaking and entering—he'd never thought she would
do such a thing. She'd always seemed to have such high
business standards. Cutthroat, but still reputable.

''I came to see the cat.''

Jordan almost missed what she had said, he was so angry. He was taking a pause for breath when she made the
simple statement.

''You what?'' He stared at her and could see that, as
unlikely as it seemed, she was telling the truth. Her blue
eyes looked huge in the dim candlelight, and her expression
was so woebegone that if he hadn't been furious with her,
he would have taken her in his arms and comforted her.
She looked so much like a forlorn waif that it made him
actually feel her pain.

Chalcie looked away from him. She didn't want to see
the pity or the anger in his eyes.

''I missed what I left behind in Boston.''

Her explanation had a disturbing ring of truth to it. He
might not like Chalcie very much, but he had a soft spot
for unhappy women and she definitely seemed to qualify.

''Boston?'' Jordan's tone was softening. He felt the anger melting away, replaced by a feeling of both concern
and unwanted interest in this woman. He reached out and
took her hand in his.

Chalcie turned her head away. She was so ashamed. She
knew that her face was red with embarrassment, and she
hated the way that he touched her. He was gentle, treating
her like a lady instead of his worst enemy. His touch was
warm, his expression kindhearted, and she wanted to throw
herself against his chest and sob for things lost long ago.

''I'm sorry. I didn't intend that you even know that I
came to your house tonight,'' Chalcie said, trying to be
dignified.

''If you had asked me, I would have invited you to my
house and let you sit with the cat as long as you wished.

I'm not an ogre, Chalcie. I am merely a man who happens to be in competition with you." Jordan's voice was deep and deceptively mild.

"I couldn't… I didn't even think…" How was she going to explain that the only plan that had come to mind was to break into his house? "I never would have broken in to look at your plans or your books."

"I think I believe you. I hope that you're telling the truth, because I've never thought of you as the kind of person who would do anything dishonorable. But you do seem to grow claws and fangs when you're around me, and I've always wondered why. Do you hate me because I've bought up land and opened businesses that are in competition with yours, or is there some other reason?"

"Isn't that enough? You are dangerous to me."

"Perhaps," Jordan said. Dangerous, but not in the way she was thinking. He wanted to touch her again. She was softer than he had expected, and the memory of the feel of her body against his this morning hadn't faded.

Despite her men's clothing, he could see the woman's softness in her face, and the fullness of her breasts. He took a deep breath, stilling the response of his body. It was out of the question to think of her this way.

"What happened when you left Boston?" Jordan sensed that if he could break down this barrier, he might understand a little more about her. He didn't want to use a weakness against her, he just wanted to know her better. "What did you leave behind?"

"Memories," Chalcie said simply. "So many people here are running away from their memories, but I have only memories to look back on. So many things were lost.…"

Jordan leaned forward, anxious for her to continue.

"Then you had a real home? Somehow, everyone who comes looking for gold seems to be a drifter. Even the women have no place to go home to. Was it like that for you?" Jordan probed. He often wondered what a young girl and her father were doing out here in this godforsaken place, when she should have been settled somewhere, married and making babies.

"Once I had a home, yes. But it's been ten years, and I don't even know if it's still there. I don't even know if those who were important to me are still alive...." Chalcie's voice trailed off. She felt strange, as if all the barriers that she had been so carefully building up had been broken down. It was a dangerous feeling, especially with Jordan de Chatain.

"I have nightmares sometimes about being stolen away. I never had a chance to say goodbye, and I hear my grandmother crying."

"And you don't even know what happened to your family?" Jordan's voice was gentle now. So that was it. Her father had stolen her away and she had never gone home again. A sudden flash of understanding hit him. No wonder she was desperate to own everything in Sonora. She hadn't understood yet that it would never replace what had been taken from her.

"I'm sorry," he said. Now he knew a little of her secret and he wished that he'd kept his questions to himself. He wanted to pull her close to him and to make the nightmares leave her forever.

Chalcie pushed back the old images. "What about you? You must have come from a family and brothers and sisters and all of that. If you hadn't, you wouldn't have built a house like this. You needed a home, too, didn't you?" Chalcie guessed shrewdly. She'd never really thought of Jordan as having a past. He'd just been her business competitor. She hadn't been curious before. Besides, in the gold country, curiosity could be dangerous.

"I did have a home, a very nice, two-story wooden house in the middle of farm country. But my story isn't nearly as interesting as yours. I was just the second son of a farmer, and I knew that there wasn't enough land to be split between Jonathan and myself. So I left."

"Were you angry about it?" she asked curiously.

Jordan shook his head. "There wasn't anything to be angry about. Dad gave me a couple of gold coins, because it was all he had. Jonathan told me he'd split the land if he had the choice, and he meant it. But I wasn't interested in being a farmer. Too many hours spent mucking out the barn, and too much work for every hour of the day. Watching fancy ladies and raking in gold is more interesting."

"And you do that very well," Chalcie said, some of her spirit beginning to reassert itself.

"Indeed I do, when I'm not plagued by a red-haired competitor. Then I spend my time watching her instead."

Chalcie blushed and then laughed as the cat finally came out of hiding and jumped into her lap.

"Do you miss your family?" she asked. "Is there someone special waiting for you to come home again?"

"No one. I'll make my own way here, and someday I'll have a wife and family. But not yet. Not quite yet," Jordan said. "The first thing I've acquired in the family department has already netted me a break-in," he teased gently.

"It was almost worth it, even being caught." Chalcie smiled.

He hesitated and then offered, "If you want to come back to visit with the cat, please let me know. You're welcome anytime."

"Thank you. But right now I think I'd better be leaving."

"May I walk you back to the C.K.? It wouldn't be right for me to let you go back alone in the dark," Jordan said, indicating another door to the alley.

Chalcie was tempted to say no, but she was still feeling fragile. She could use a strong male hand on her arm for a few moments.

Jordan led her down the steps and onto the main road until they came to her small room at the back of the saloon. He gazed down at her and seemed almost to think of kissing her, until he drew back at the last moment.

Chalcie didn't notice when two miners stopped and gawked at the two of them and then began whispering.

Within an hour everyone in Sonora knew that Jordan and Chalcie had been out together. Within two hours, the miners had Chalcie and Jordan almost married and the C.K. and Dry Gulch consolidated into the biggest and best saloon this side of San Francisco. By morning, Chalcie's father had heard about the budding romance and was ready to take steps to keep his little girl safe from Jordan de Chatain.

Chapter Two

"Chalcie, wake up!"

Someone was pounding on the rough boards that served to separate Chalcie's sleeping quarters from the bar.

"Go away," Chalcie moaned. She'd only been in bed for a few minutes, she was certain. It had been too hot in the gold rush town even to think about sleeping until the night was nearly half-finished. Even her hair, bound up in tight braids to keep it off her neck, felt hot, as if the burnished red of her hair had transmuted itself into sultry summer heat.

"Right now, daughter," James Kent ordered. "Come on, girl, and give us some of that fine whiskey. I know you have it hidden in the trunk!" He thumped his fist against the rough wooden siding that served for the three solid walls of Chalcedony's bedroom. The fourth wall of red calico swayed with the onslaught.

Chalcie swore bitterly under her breath as she struggled to sit up. It was the middle of the night, and her father wanted better whiskey than was served from the bar? Well, he wasn't going to get it from her!

"I'm sleeping. Go away," Chalcie yelled again. She hoped it worked. Most of the time she could count on her father giving up after a few nasty complaints about insolent daughters.

"I want to drink a toast with my new partner, and I'm going to use the good stuff, not the rotgut you have in those barrels out back."

"Oh, God," Chalcie moaned. "Please, not another partner."

Her stomach suddenly hurt. She'd lived through enough of her father's partners to know that he never picked winners. Her father seemed to attract people who recognized and played on his weaknesses. Over the years she had been starved, shot at and run out of town because of his partners. Even though Houlihan wasn't a partner, he was typical of the men that her father chose for important jobs like buying supplies in Stockton and bringing them back to Sonora. Losers, every one of them.

"Damn, just when everything was beginning to go well." Chalcie made a fist and struck at the blanket that served as a mattress on her bed. For the first time since her father had stolen her from her grandparents' house in Boston, Chalcedony had felt safe. They had enough money to live on and they had stayed in one place for more than six months. Everything would be fine if her father didn't bring in someone who would mess things up and take half the profits.

"Now!" her father yelled.

Chalcie sighed. She stood up and opened her one small trunk. The flat yellow bottle of good whiskey was nestled against the pretty rosebud pink paper that lined the trunk.

Another partner and more trouble.

Chalcie and James Kent had come to the gold country with nothing. They'd stayed in San Francisco long enough to collect a few essential items they would need to find gold in the hills and then had set out for Sonora. For the first time, James Kent had sworn that he'd strike out without a partner, and to Chalcie's surprise, he had actually done it. For the first time, instead of disaster, her father had brought them wealth. They had traveled down out of the mountains and back to San Francisco once, laden with gold that her father had found. They had been giddy with joy and surprise. After ten years, James Kent had found something he could do. He could witch gold from the ground.

Chalcie took the whiskey bottle out of the trunk and wished that she had had the foresight to go to Johnny Tong and ask for some kind of potion to put in the whiskey to make her father forget all his crazy notions like needing a partner. Johnny Tong had a reputation for making up herb potions that could cure the grippe, banish unspeakable diseases and make men forget their wildest dreams. But the whiskey was nothing but whiskey, and she'd refused to answer her father as long as she dared.

Her father knocked again perfunctorily and then strode into the room, a fine figure of a man. As usual, he was wearing his black frock coat and the white ruffled shirt that he had decided gave him a distinguished appearance. After all, he was a gold witch, a man who could find gold wherever he looked. He was better than the miners in their dusty pants made from the sails of ships marooned in San Francisco harbor. James Kent was special and he intended to remind them of it. His dark red hair was pomaded and carefully combed to make certain no one suspected it was thinning on the top. But even he couldn't hide the frosting of white hair on his heavy eyebrows or the lines on his face and around his eyes from years in the sun.

"It's about time, daughter. Now, I want you to meet Pete Ames." Her father pulled the curtain open further and gestured for the man waiting outside to enter.

"Chalcie, this is Pete Ames, and he's my new partner."

Pete Ames stepped into the room and bowed with a long sweeping motion. "Pleased to meet you, Chalcie. I've heard so much about you these last few days."

Pete Ames's voice was cultured and smooth. His face was handsome and well-defined. His pale blond hair was an artful tumble of curls, and he was obviously quite the dandy with his black coat and blue vest and fine gold watch. No one carried a watch out here—time didn't have much meaning to the miners.

Chalcie looked at him and frowned. Why did he make her want to back away from him? He was good-looking, but there was something about the man that made her teeth itch.

"Pete is brand-new to town, and he's never even been out to a dig. I figured on taking him with me for the next week. When we come back, I'll see about him taking over the books and other business that you've been handling." Her father said it blandly, as if he didn't expect any argument at all from Chalcie. "Pete's an attorney, and since things are getting citylike around here, I figured that the only way to protect myself from grabbers was to make certain that the law was on my side."

Pete Ames stood there, a half smile on his handsome face, while her father explained the new relationship. It was obvious that he didn't expect any trouble from Chalcie. After all, she was just a girl.

Chalcie watched Pete Ames. For all his slickness and congeniality, the man reminded her of a snake. The eyes were the same as those of the rattlers that came out to soak up the heat from the rocks at night—cold and black and hard. Ames could move his mouth in a smile, but it never touched the rest of his face.

Ames smiled modestly as he listened to Kent extolling his virtues to Chalcie. He watched every move that Chalcie made.

When her father stopped, Ames stepped into the silence. "I can help. I know what the people in San Francisco are doing, and that's where most of the real legal troubles happen, not out here. So I'd be a perfect partner to keep your father safe. He's protected here and in San Francisco. Just what a man like him needs."

Chalcie almost snorted.

"Ah, do I see a doubt in your pretty green eyes?"

"They're not green," Chalcie snapped. "And you see a lot more than doubt."

James Kent poured two full tumblers of whiskey and handed one to Pete. "To our partnership, may it be long and fruitful," he intoned, and then drank down the libation in one long gulp. He ignored Chalcie. He had long ago decided that there were some fights he couldn't win with his daughter, so he tried to stay clear of her when she had that look in her eyes. Pete was his partner and if she didn't like it, she could leave.

"We'll talk about this in the morning, when you're sober," Chalcie said frostily. Her father wasn't going to get away with this. He needed to be reminded that she—and no one else—was his partner.

"I'm sober now," her father said, raising his voice in exasperation. He poured more of the whiskey into his glass.

"No, you are not, and I'm not going to try and talk sense to you while you're in this condition. Go up to the room above the bakery and sleep it off and then come back," Chalcie ordered. "Partner, indeed. We'll see about that."

"We will not. What makes you think you have anything to say about it?" her father challenged her belligerently.

Chalcie drew a deep breath. This was the last straw. She'd bailed him out so many times she'd lost count. Each problem had been caused in some way by a partner, and now he was questioning her right to say anything?

James Kent saw the set of her chin and the fire in her eyes and decided to stop her before she could erupt in another tirade about his behavior. He jutted his head forward, glaring at Chalcedony. "Not even a whisper from you, Chalcie. You don't know the rumors that are going around town tonight. People are talking about you and Jordan de Chatain, my worst enemy. At least Pete Ames is my friend."

Her father turned to leave, but Pete Ames stayed behind for a moment.

"Watch out, Chalcedony. I think you'll find I have ways

of making things happen. Don't fight too hard, or you might not like what happens.''

Chalcie looked over at her father, hoping that he had heard the words, but the man wasn't listening to anything that Pete said. He was nursing his grudge against her.

"Don't you try and threaten me," Chalcie snapped.

"It's not a threat. It's the truth," Pete said, and smiled his reptilian smile again.

The calico fell before Chalcie could answer him.

Chalcie felt sick, and it wasn't just the heat. She walked over to the rough pine bed and sat down, because she was certain that her legs weren't steady enough to hold her. She couldn't sleep. She'd seen the face of her nemesis and it frightened her. She couldn't wipe Pete Ames's superior smile and cold blue eyes out of her mind.

Pete Ames was going to destroy her. He had been measuring her, thinking of how he was going to make certain that she wasn't a threat to him. He already had her father flummoxed, but he knew that she wouldn't be so easy to deceive. She would have to be careful of this man or he could take everything she'd worked for. Indeed, she would have preferred to see her father become partners with Jordan de Chatain; at least he was a known quantity.

The air was stifling with the late summer heat, and finally Chalcie gave up on the idea of going back to sleep. If only she could turn off the turmoil in her mind, she might be able to rest.

"How could I have been so stupid?" she berated herself, recalling her father's mention of the rumors about her and Jordan. She hadn't been thinking clearly. For the first time in ten years she'd allowed her emotions to rule instead of her brains and look where it had landed her. The damage to her reputation might already have been done.

Chalcie pulled back the calico curtain and tied it so that some fresh air could enter the room. What resources did she have at hand to make certain that she and her father wouldn't be skinned alive while Pete Ames walked away with everything?

Maybe she was overreacting. Maybe there was nothing to worry about. But long experience told her that the best fight was won with the most preparation. She was going to be prepared for this one, even if it never happened.

"If I were laying a wager, though, I'd give ten to one that Pete and I will come to blows about what my father can and cannot sign away to him," Chalcie muttered. "So the best thing I can do is find out what I can hold on to and what my father can give away."

Chalcie took down the ledger from the rough shelf that had been nailed on the wall and lighted another tin can lamp.

Normally the numbers showing a profit would have lulled her, soothed her with promises that she would never be poor again. This time, however, all she could see were the hours and days and months of sweating and working that could be ruined in an instant by her father.

Then she dug further, looking back at what she had thought was a reasonable and prudent way of preserving their money. Her father had brought the gold in, and Chalcie had invested it. First one lot and then the second, and then a bar and a bakery to serve the miners. Her holdings had increased. They'd never had a lot of ready money around, because just as soon as Chalcie accumulated a few hundred dollars, she invested it into land, buildings or supplies. Not only did their holdings increase, but managing the money that way served another purpose—it kept James Kent's hands off the gold. He couldn't gamble it away, he couldn't drink it away, he couldn't touch it.

Or at least that was what Chalcie had thought until she had time to sit down and actually read through the documents and look over the books.

"I have nothing," Chalcie said, stunned by the realization. "If my father decides to give it all away, I'll be a pauper again." She stared at the wall, seeing the image of her future security fading. Everything that she had worked for was in her father's name. There wasn't even a piece of land, a pouch of gold, or a keg of whiskey in her name. The Kent fortunes weren't hers, they were James Kent's, and he had no intention of sharing with the person who had made the fortune for him.

Chalcie put the ledger away and began to pace the tiny space. Three steps one way and three steps the other, not enough to release any of her pent-up frustration.

"I have to get out of here."

Chalcie stepped out into the darkness. She touched the rough wood as she worked her way around to the back of the building, where she could sit on the stump that Jordan had offered her the day before. If she just sat quietly, in the early morning darkness, she could try to think through her choices.

"Choices—ha! As if I had any," she muttered. Of course she couldn't ignore the fact that she should have insisted that at least half of the property be placed in her name. Instead of allowing James Kent to forget what he owed her, she should have reminded him every single day of his debt to her.

She did have one choice that would shock her father. She could run away from home and go live with the Miwok Indians who were native to the area. She could find a place to sleep near Estelle's fire, and she knew enough about living off the land from her own experience and the Indians' tutoring that she wouldn't starve.

Chalcie smiled. Her father would never expect her just to leave him in favor of living with Estelle and the Indians. The idea had a certain charm to it.

"Ow! Damn it," she swore as she touched the wall and drove a splinter from the wooden siding into her fingertip. She sucked at her finger as she continued down the alley-way. She found the stump and sat down, wishing that the newly washed pink calico gave her more protection against the stub ends left by the saw. She stared up at the stars and tried to blank out the sounds of the miners as she concentrated on her various problems.

She had been sitting for almost an hour, trying to find a way to make her father stop his destructive plans, when she heard the sound of boots crunching in the dirt and rock-filled area behind Jordan's Dry Gulch Saloon. It was obvious that the men didn't think anyone else was in the area, because they weren't making any particular effort to be quiet as they moved around the building. One man carried a tin can candle that gave out almost no light. They lurched against the side of the building, using it to prop themselves up as they tried to find the back of the saloon.

"Over here, Jedidiah, this is the place. And just about here ought to wipe him out...." One miner hiccuped. He could barely make himself understood, he was so drunk. "See, it'll go right up and over the top and no one will have a chance, least of all Mr. Smart Ass Himself de Chatain."

"Yeah, telling us we were cheating at the table. We don't need to cheat, we're the best in the business," the other man said, slurring his words.

"What'll we use to start it with?"

The other man was silent for a few seconds as he looked around him with drink-blurred eyes.

"What's wrong with one of these candles and a few of those pieces of wood left over from the buildings?" he asked belligerently.

"You get the wood. I'll clear a space so that it'll take off good and fast and hot."

The man named Jedidiah knelt down and began to move rocks and other debris from the back of the building. He moved with the exaggerated slowness of a drunk. He reached around him and took great handfuls of tall dry weeds, and soon he had a pile gathered at the base of the tar paper and wood building.

"Anyone comes back here, shoot 'em," the second miner said. "No one's going to stop us this time."

Chalcie was too stunned to move. At first she had thought they were just harmless drunks. But these men were serious about starting a fire.

She watched in horror as they moved around the clearing. What was she going to do? If she moved, they'd grab her, knock her unconscious and leave her for dead. She might wake up and then again she might not, depending on how the fire burned. Or they might just shoot her. She could have eased to the right and up the side of the bar, but she was mortally afraid of attracting their attention. If they saw the flash of movement, she'd be dead.

"I can't just sit here… I've got to think of a way out of this…." If Jordan's place burned, the whole town could go up in flames.

The second miner lurched and cursed and then began to pick up the shavings of wood and small sticks and branches that had been left from the construction months ago. They were brittle and dry, snapping as he gathered them.

"Good, good, now a few more pieces, but bigger. We've got to give this a good start."

"I'll drag that limb over—there are dead leaves at the top. Ought to go like a firecracker!"

"*Whoosh*, it's gonna go *whoosh!*" Jedidiah cackled, throwing his arms upward.

Chalcie closed her eyes, offering up a quick prayer that whatever she did, it would be enough. She tensed, ready to jump and run, when she heard the sound of a can being tossed into the pile. Time had just run out.

"Damn you!" she screamed as she saw the flames begin to lick at the base of the building.

The men turned on her, their faces clearly outlined in the rising flames.

"Shoot her!" Jedidiah yelled.

"Damn! What's she doing there?"

The men stared at her, too stunned to shoot.

"I don't know what she's doing, but let's get the hell away from here."

The men ran, stumbling and cursing each other, trying to get away from Chalcie. She heard their boots thudding down the dusty street.

"Fire! Help someone—fire!" she screamed, breaking the terrible paralysis that had held her as she stared at the two men.

There was a crackle as the flames began to spread from the dry weeds, which crumpled and disappeared, to the tinder dry wood.

"Fire! Fire!" No one was responding. No one could hear her over the fights and yelling and all the other noise of the town.

"Damn you, oh, damn you all to hell!" Chalcie sobbed as she ran toward the fire. She had to stop it before it really took hold of the wood, or the town was doomed. She reached into the flames trying to pull the burning embers apart and break the flames that were hissing against the back of the pine slats.

"I can't do it," she cried as the flames licked up her fingers. Her shirt was already smoldering, and she knew she fought a losing battle. She looked around frantically for something, anything she could smother the fire with. But there wasn't a tarp or a piece of blanket or anything else close by.

She picked up a discarded piece of board and began to beat at the base of the fire.

"Fire! God, can't anyone hear me? Fire!" Chalcie screamed again and again, but there was no answer.

The flames were winning. If they managed to climb the heavy branch that the men had placed against the wall, she knew that it would be all over. Throwing down the board, she grabbed the limb and tried to heave it out of the way, but it was too heavy for her.

Sweat was pouring down her, soaking her, and she didn't want to feel the prickling that meant her hands had been burned.

Then, in the flickering of the fire, she saw salvation. Jordan rounded the corner of the saloon, closely followed by a contingent of the men from the bar, all of them ready to help. She heard a mutter from one of the men, a horrible idea that quickly spread to the other men.

"Chalcie started the fire. She was back here and she started the trouble."

Jordan heard it, but didn't waste any time on questions. "Quick, get the water from the barrels!"

Against the rough wooden frame of the bar there were two huge barrels of water that Jordan kept on hand for washup and other bar duties. There would be water in them. Water would stop the fire.

Chalcie ran to the barrels, grabbing the pail that sat to one side of the containers. Jordan was right beside her, his face sweating in the heat, which was made even more intense by the fire.

She reached up and pulled the drum toward her and heard the sickening sound of just a few inches of water sloshing in the bottom. Jordan's hands closed over hers as they pulled the container toward the fire.

"Please, it's not enough," she whimpered. It might slow the fire down, but it wouldn't stop it.

She tilted the barrel, straining under the heavy water-soaked wood, and reached as far as she could into the interior to fill the bucket.

"Move, we'll get it!" She was pushed aside, and the men hoisted the barrel on their shoulders and threw the water on the flames that were licking greedily at the wood.

There was a hissing and she saw the flames begin to recede, but they didn't die. It wasn't enough. The building was charring and smouldering. There was a sick feeling in the pit of her stomach as she realized that within a few seconds the fire would turn into a conflagration.

"Get more men, get buckets, we've got to stop this now!" Jordan ordered.

Chalcie seized the edge of the second drum and almost wept in relief as she felt the heaviness of the water inside.

"Jordan, this one has more water!"

Jordan was instantly beside her, plunging his hand into the lukewarm wetness. "It'll have to do."

"Give me containers. Take this pail. We've got enough water here!" she yelled, and a man responded by grabbing the pail from her hands. But no one had anything more to use as a scoop, and she found herself pushed aside again as the men seized the filled barrel and pulled it directly toward the fire. Chalcie gripped one of the edges and pulled. The muscles in her arms ached with the effort, and she knew that come morning—if there was a morning for the town—she wouldn't be able to move. Her fingers clenched around the rusted iron belt that held the cask together, and she pulled the barrel closer to the fire. The heavy container bucked and gritted against the rocks, digging a path in the dirt.

The flames were higher now. The building was going to go. There wasn't any more time to get the barrel into position or think about the niceties of rationing the water to pailfuls at a time. It would require the whole cask to put this out, if they were lucky; she didn't want to think about what would happen if they weren't.

Chalcie helped tip the keg, pushing with all her might, and let the water gush out in a huge wave that rushed over the fire and up the wall, quenching the flames completely. The force of the water and the weight of the barrel managed to dislodge the heavy limb and break the contact with the tar paper roof. A gout of steam reached upward, almost obscuring the building.

A ragged cheer went up from the men. The fire was out.

Chalcie slumped over the barrel and let the sobs of relief and terror wash over her just as the water had washed over the flames. She had done it. She had helped stop the fire, even though she hadn't been able to stop the men from starting it.

"What the hell happened?"

"How did it start?"

"You think Chalcie did it, to wipe Jordan out of business?"

"Yeah, that new dancer really cut into her profits, and if she couldn't get the gold, maybe she didn't want anyone to have it." The voices were getting rougher, angrier. There was a dangerous murmur from the crowd as the men began to believe what they were saying, even though there was no evidence that it was the truth.

Slowly Chalcie registered what the men were saying. The shock and numbness began to wear off and anger washed over her. She'd been fighting the fire before they ever came on the scene, and they thought she'd started it? How could they? Chalcie waited for Jordan to come to her rescue, to tell the men that she could never do such a thing. The words didn't come.

"Chalcie?" Jordan leaned over her and placed a hand on her shoulder. To Chalcie, it felt like the hand of doom. What would she do if he thought she was capable of such a thing?

"What happened?" he asked in a grave tone.

Chalcie wiped her eyes with her filthy hands and stood up to face her accusers. She looked at Jordan, hoping that his face would be friendly, but his expression was wary and watchful. That hurt more than anything. How could he think, even for a moment, that she was capable of destroying Sonora out of a fit of jealousy?

"I was sitting out here, just trying to think through a problem, when two men sneaked around to the back of the saloon. They were men you accused of cheating, Jordan. I guess they were in the bar earlier this evening."

She looked at him, hoping to see a glimmer of recognition in his eyes. Surely he would remember such a thing, wouldn't he?

She could see the expression on his face, the closed look that he had, and she knew with a sinking heart that he didn't believe her. He didn't remember the two men who had actually started the fire. He thought she was guilty.

"Okay, men, let's go back into the bar. There's nothing more happening out here. We're all safe." Whether Chalcie was guilty or innocent, Jordan knew that if he didn't act quickly, the men were liable to do something they would regret later. There'd never been a woman strung up in the gold country, but in the heat of anger and passions, it could happen. He didn't want that to happen to Chalcie because a few hotheads went out of control.

"I'll look for these guys, just in case she's telling the truth," Brad McClatchy said.

Chalcie heard the jeering from the back of the crowd. They didn't want to believe her. They wanted trouble.

"Thank you, Brad," Chalcie said. She lifted her head and started to walk through the crowd. Suddenly Jordan was at her right side, taking her arm, giving her the protection she needed to walk through unharmed. Chalcie looked up at him and saw that his expression hadn't changed. He might not believe her, but he did feel some responsibility for her safety.

Chalcie felt tears begin to betray her. She hurt, she was tired, it had been a rotten day, and every bone in her body ached. But she wouldn't cry in front of him; she refused to let him see that weakness. If he didn't know that she'd done him a favor by saving him from the fire, she certainly wasn't going to tell him. There wasn't any love lost between them, anyway.

As they stopped in front of her room, Jordan finally spoke. His voice was rough with anger. "I don't understand this, Chalcie. I don't know what happened, but I do know that earlier this evening I was feeling sorry for you. I heard some of the men gossiping and I actually flattened some guy when he suggested that there was something going on between us. I cared about your good name. Is this the thanks I get?"

Chalcie gasped at the unfairness of his attack. "I never did, and I never would do, such a thing. Those men will be found, and then won't you and the others have something to be sorry for!''

She pulled the curtain off the hook, shutting it in his face. She had never been so hurt in her life.

Chalcie threw herself, fully dressed, down on the bed. It was only a few hours to sunrise, and suddenly she couldn't even move. She was bone weary, emotionally drained and too exhausted even to be angry with Jordan. Although she knew she should be bathing her hands in tea, she was too tired. If her palms blistered and burned and she couldn't work for a few days, it served her father right.

She just didn't care anymore.

Chapter Three

Chalcie pushed aside the last tendrils of her nightmares and opened her eyes. She looked around at the familiar room. From her low, rough wooden bed, she could see underneath the bottom of the calico curtain and directly into the street filled with miners and burros. The pack animals and the miners were about equally laden, carrying pans, ropes and the ubiquitous chamois bags waiting to be filled with gold.

There was a smell of singed wood in the air, and it brought back memories of the night before in a terrible rush. The fire. Jordan believing the men when they said she could have actually started it herself. Her father and his new partner. All of it jumbled together into one painful lump that made her groan as she thought about the day ahead. She still had to get up, though. She had work to do and she'd have to ignore the looks and the remarks meant to hurt her. They'd forget the absurd idea that she'd started the fire soon enough.

Chalcie began to push herself up and then screamed as the pain lanced through her. She fell back against the blanket, sobbing as she tried to move her hands, and realized they were so burned that she couldn't bear to flex them or touch them. She held them up to look at the burns and saw that they weren't as bad as they might have been. From the pain she had expected to see blackened skin and blisters covering her whole hand. Instead, there were two long burns across the palms of her hands and on her left wrist. The flesh had blistered and the skin was raised in ugly red spots with some of them turning to white.

"Well, maybe it's a little too late for the tea treatment," Chalcie said, this time moving more carefully as she stood up. She tried her hands again and found that, once she was expecting the pain, she could actually move the fingers all right, and if she bandaged the palms of her hands, she might be able to carry on at least some of her work.

She'd go and find out whether her father had actually taken Ames prospecting. Then she'd face the men of the town and lay to rest those awful rumors. She didn't know how she was going to do it, but she had to make them see that she would never have stooped to that kind of treachery.

Chalcie brushed her hair and managed to confine the recalcitrant red curls into some semblance of order. She hoped that her father hadn't really set out to find the mother lode with Pete Ames, but then she never knew what to expect from James Kent.

Finally, she gave up on her hair and concentrated on cleansing her raw skin. Washing her face and arms made her realize that burns and water weren't a pleasant combination, but she persisted just long enough to remove the smudges left by the smoke.

The heavy curtain was low enough that she had some privacy, but not much. She longed for a real bath, with lots of water and plenty of soap. She knew already that only a real bath was going to get rid of the singed scent that lingered around her. And cold water might make her hands ache, but she knew it would probably do some good to her reddened skin.

"Chalcie, you up yet?" Ted banged on one of the rough-cut logs that served to brace the walls. The pine planks shook alarmingly. The long low-slung building had been constructed in two days and had none of the solid bracing that could have been found in a building expected to last more than one or two seasons. Ted knocked again before Chalcie had a chance to answer.

"All right, wait a minute…I'm coming." Chalcie painfully wound the piece of twine that she used to tie her hair back and looped it around the thick red mass. It would serve to keep her neck cool, and that was all she cared about. She slipped into the same dress, happy that it had been made without buttons.

Chalcie pulled back the curtain and stepped out into the daylight. It was marginally cooler outside.

"Your father said to tell you he'll be back in a week's time. He and Pete Ames left at first light," Ted stated flatly.

"Bread's on," he continued, "and rising over at the bakery. I'm heading out for the hills and don't expect me to be back for a week or so. Damon said he'd come in to do the kneading tomorrow, but you'd better keep an eye on him. Damon's not one that I'd trust with doing more than throwing in the flour, yeast and water and calling it done. Men won't buy hardtack, and that's what he'd serve them."

He shifted uneasily.

"I just wanted to tell you that I know you didn't start the fire. I think I know who the men are that you saw, and some of the miners are trying to track them down this morning."

"Thank you, Ted," Chalcie said, grateful for the words of comfort. At least some people knew her well enough to realize she would never start a fire that could have devastated the whole town.

Chalcie knew she could have spent time fretting about what had happened, but there wasn't any use in doing so. She still had the business to run.

"Okay, the bread's on. What about the beer? Has anyone sampled that one keg we've got going in the back of the room? The last batch was a little too powerful. Too much sugar, I guess."

"I checked it last night. Drank a little. It needs to be

moved to another cask, and then it's ready to serve. We've only had one explosion. I'm still on the lookout for someone who really knows how to make beer," Ted added. "And a baker who is better than Damon, too."

"Good luck," Chalcie said. "They'll all be out looking for gold, same as you."

Ted had the grace to look ashamed of running out on his job. "Yes, but I can't help but try. You being a woman and all, and having to run the bakery, you don't have the urge to get out there and find gold. It's easy for you to stay in town. At least I let you know I was going to leave."

"I know, and I appreciate it, not to mention your confidence in my innocence," Chalcie said. She wished that Jordan had shown the same kind of faith in her. But he hadn't, and she had the feeling that even if they caught the men, Jordan would rather die and go to hell before he'd admit that he might have been wrong.

Just like most men, she decided.

"I'll be going then, if you can handle it," Ted said. He bobbed his head in a brief bow and left her, walking up toward the mines.

Chalcie turned away toward the store and the bakery. She sighed, thinking of the work ahead of her the next week. She'd have been happy to double Ted's wages just to keep him in the bakery, but she hadn't even tried. Once the gold fever hit, there was no way to keep a man out of the fields. At least he was conscientious enough to tell her he was leaving. More than once her workers had left without so much as a wave of the hand.

She trudged down the hills toward the bakery and store, which were perched on the edge of the creek that served most of the town's needs for water. She had bought the land hoping that the creek would serve for the bakery and store, but the water quality had deteriorated so fast that she had taken to having carts of water brought in for any food preparation. Even then she wasn't certain that it was clean. There were other miners above her source. Still, anything was better than the turbulent water from the winter creek, or the almost mudlike trickle that the creek had become this summer.

She was so busy thinking about the bread, the trouble with her father and that awful partner of his that she almost didn't see Brad McClatchy as he hurried toward her. She had just about reached the conclusion that nothing more terrible could possibly happen to her, when Brad caught up with her. What more could the man want? He'd already eaten, slept and dressed at her expense, all because she wanted a piece of land that he owned. She wasn't ready to give him too much more.

"Chalcie, wait for me, please." Brad McClatchy puffed up behind her, his skinny face red with the exertion. The sweat was coursing down from his forehead, even though the day was barely started. The real heat wouldn't hit for several more hours. As usual, Brad looked half on the verge of dying from exertion.

Chalcie had never understood why Brad had come to the California hills. He was tiny, well under five feet, and he was frail. He should have been at home some place, allowing the women in his family to look after him. Instead, he had been trying to scratch out a living in the gold country and barely succeeding. The only thing that Brad had managed to do right was take a claim on a piece of land that turned out to be right in the middle of Sonora, on the busiest street. There were saloons on both sides of Brad's lot, and everyone in Sonora had to pass in front of it at least twice a day. It was a prime piece of land and Chalcedony wanted it. She had placed a bid six months ago and even paid a fee to Brad for letting her keep the right to buy for the next year. He had been living off that money for the last six months. Best of all, her father knew nothing of the deal.

"How can I help you, Brad?" Chalcie said pleasantly. She had already changed her mind about not advancing any more money and decided that if he wanted more money to

keep the land open, he could have it. That land might be
the one item that she was able to keep back from her father
if he and Pete Ames began to split up the Kent holdings.
The lot between de Chatain's Dry Gulch Saloon and her
own C. K. Saloon was worth almost anything Brad wanted
to ask for it.

"They found the men—you know, that Jedidiah and his
friend? They were trying to sneak out of town at first dawn,
but they were so drunk they slept too late, and they were
spotted as they tried to hike out the back way. The men
have them chained to the front porch of the Dry Gulch."
Brad panted and then fanned himself as he stopped under
the shade of one of the big valley oak trees that stood almost in the middle of the street.

"They found them?" Chalcie felt her spirits lift. At least
someone had believed her. Someone had to have remembered the two cheating miners in the Dry Gulch. She smiled
grimly. Now Jordan would have to realize that he should
have trusted her.

Brad tried to catch his breath, and Chalcie could hear a
painful wheeze that seemed to originate deep in his lungs
and rattle until he finally finished exhaling. It was not a
pleasant sound.

"Thank you for telling me. I just wish you hadn't hurried. I worry when you can't catch your breath," Chalcie
said.

"I needed to talk to you about something else, too,
though the men were the most important." He stopped and
gasped a few more times. "I have to go home. I can't
breathe here," he said, laboring to get every word out. "I
came to California thinking I could live here. But it's just
getting worse." Every time Brad exhaled, he moaned
slightly. "I have to sell that land now. I need the money
to go home."

Chalcie closed her eyes. She had coveted that land since
Brad bought it but she still didn't have enough to buy it
outright. She had hoped he was only going to tell her that

he needed a little more money and that he'd appreciated the times he'd been allowed to come into the boarding-house or the bakery and take what he needed without paying. Chalcie hadn't expected him to say that he needed the money and was ready to leave Sonora forever.

"I'd be glad to stake you to some more money, if that's what you need. I can buy a little more time for you," Chalcie offered, trying to see if he could be dissuaded from returning to the States right now.

If he insisted on cash today, or even this month, she knew she wouldn't be able to meet his price. She'd already revised, juggled and swore over the books last night. She'd tried everything she could to think of a way to salvage some resources from the partnership that her father was forming with Pete Ames. But everything was tied up. Even though it had been a good summer, every pinch of gold they had taken in had gone to buy goods down in Stockton, or even in San Francisco. She had poured more and more money into land and supplies to keep the money out of her father's hands. Expenses were high, and even though prices were higher, the Kents were rich in land, buildings and businesses—but not ready cash.

Brad was shaking his head ruefully. "Thanks for the offer. You've helped me a lot these last few months. But I don't want to stay here anymore. I want to go home."

"How soon?" she asked faintly.

"How soon do I go home?"

"No, how soon do you need the money?"

"Within the next week. I want to get out of here and down to San Francisco. They say there'll be a ship leaving to go back to the States. I want to be on it."

"You need two thousand dollars in gold by the end of the week?" Chalcie was hoping he'd say no, it was only a joke. But from the looks of him, he wasn't joking.

"That's right," Brad wheezed. Even though he stood in the shade, his thin face was still red from the exertion of trying to breathe. "If you can't buy it, I understand. I have another person who is interested," Brad admitted hesitantly.

He could see the shock that his announcement had given Chalcedony. He would have let her have all the time she needed, if he had been able to. But for months there hadn't been a ship that came into the San Francisco harbor and left again. No captain could keep men on board once they heard about the gold that was to be found in the hills and streams of California. So far, every ship that had sailed into the harbor had been left to rot until it either sank or was converted into a floating whorehouse, saloon or jail. But the *Maybird* was rumored to have a good chance of leaving San Francisco—the captain had chosen his men all from his own relatives!

Chalcie bit her lip. She didn't have two thousand in cash. She had only enough gold on hand to send someone down to Stockton for more supplies for the store and the saloon. That was eight hundred dollars and the driver's fee. Not enough by half to pay Brad what he was asking for the land. There wasn't any way she could possibly get her hands on that amount of cash.

"Who is the other buyer?" Chalcie had one shred of hope left—maybe she could work out a deal with the other buyer. He'd put up the cash and then she would have a chance to redeem it from him for the price plus twenty percent. She was certain she'd have access to that much gold when her father returned from his time in the mountains. Twenty percent profit for a few weeks' use of the money would not be a bad deal for most men. Surely there wasn't a man in all of Sonora who would turn down that deal. Hope began to light her eyes again.

"The other buyer is Jordan de Chatain."

Chalcie sighed as the hope died. Yes, there was one man who would refuse to sell, even for a hundred percent profit. Jordan de Chatain. He'd been lusting after that very piece of property for months. She had heard from several very reliable sources that he had said he would buy it if he ever got the chance. She knew that she'd never manage to pry Jordan's paws off it once he gained the claim.

"Damn," she muttered faintly, low enough so that Brad couldn't hear her through his wheezing.

She had to think of something. She could feel the land slipping through her grasp. Her only chance to save something outside of the partnership with Ames, and the richest woman in Sonora wasn't going to be able to buy a lot for only two thousand dollars.

Brad watched the play of emotions on her face. He was sorry for her, but he had to leave, and if she couldn't pay, Jordan could.

"Think about it. I'm not leaving until Sunday night. That's a whole week away, and I'll hold it until Sunday afternoon."

"Thanks, Brad," Chalcie said. She hurried on down toward the bakery.

She stared down at the ground as she walked, wishing that she could find a fist-size piece of gold in the well-worn pathway. That would solve all of her problems. Unfortunately, she knew that she wasn't a gold witch like her father. If she found a nugget that size, sure as hell someone else would come whooping and hollering back up the trail, looking for the gold they'd dropped. That was the way her luck was running. Neither gold nor luck came easily to her.

Chalcie pushed the idea of gold from her mind. There were too many other things to be done for her to daydream about something she couldn't have. The bread was still waiting to be baked. She needed to make out a supplies list to be sent to Stockton with her pack train. She had to make certain that the new batch of whiskey that had just been brought in was good.

There was no easy way out of the dilemma handed to her by her father. All morning long, as she baked the bread that had been left kneaded and rising, then sold it to the miners, she turned the problem over in her mind.

After the last loaf of bread had been sold and the ovens were cooling, Chalcie finally took time to walk outside into the shimmering heat of the day.

She could smell the heavy cedar scent that surrounded the town. The sky was relentlessly blue, and, in the hazy distance, the mountains danced as the heat waves rose from the rifts and valleys. The stream had dried to a trickle. She needed another three barrels of water before the next morning's baking and more for the cleanup of the bar when the last miner finally went outside to sleep off his excesses. She'd have to ask Juanita to keep her eyes open for someone who looked as if he could use a few pinches of gold in payment for hauling water.

She wondered if Jordan had filled up his own barrels yet, since they'd been dumped to douse the fire. And what was he thinking, she wondered, now that the men who had really started the fire were chained to his front rail. Was he regretting his hasty judgment of her?

She sighed. He'd have to deal with his problems. She had her own, and one of them was getting the barrels filled. It wasn't difficult to fill the containers at the stream that flowed with clear sweet water up the hill about a mile and a half from town, but most miners weren't interested in any job other than mining.

Chalcie and Juanita constantly watched for someone who had spent their last gold and didn't even have enough for a meal—those were the men who would take on the job and fill the barrels. Of course there was another possibility. The young Mexican miner, Eduardo. He was always hanging around Juanita like a puppy.

Chalcie had watched the way that he looked at Juanita when she was working, and it was obvious that he was dreaming dreams of love and romance. She wondered if her friend had even noticed Eduardo. Juanita didn't react to men the way the rest of the women in Sonora did. She kept to herself, talked to men as necessary to keep them in line, but she never allowed anyone to become personal with her. Some of the men, she knew, called Juanita the Mexican ice maiden.

Juanita could stand a little romance in her life, Chalcie thought, and Eduardo would have been a fine man to have a romance with. Eduardo was different. Shy, likable, soft-spoken and never drunk. She'd have to talk to Juanita about the man, maybe even give the two of them a push so that they'd be together at least for a while.

Chalcie put the thought aside. If no one else needed money from filling the barrels, she knew that Eduardo would do the favor gladly, just for the chance to impress Juanita.

Her hands ached from the burns and the abuse that she had given them this morning. She had dropped two loaves of bread because she hadn't anticipated the searing pain that lanced through her when she touched anything warm. She hadn't been able to clean the bakery after the baking; the blistered skin hurt too badly to be immersed again in water. She shivered as she tried to stretch her abused hands.

''Heat's getting to you?''

Chalcie tensed, her back rigid. That was the last voice in the world she wanted to hear.

Jordan de Chatain!

She turned toward him, wishing she could close her eyes and disappear.

''Are you all right?'' Jordan's voice carried a note of concern. He reached for her and then drew back his hand. After last night she would have every reason to punch him just as solidly as she could, and he had no doubt that she swung a powerful left hook when provoked.

Chalcedony opened her eyes. ''I'm fine,'' she said tiredly.

Jordan looked down at the ground and kicked the toe of his shiny black boot in the dust. He scuffed for a few seconds and then looked at Chalcie. It was obvious from his expression that he was uncomfortable.

Chalcie didn't care how he felt. She was sick and tired

of men, all men, and this man in particular. "Mr. de Cha-tain, I've had a miserable twenty-four hours. My hands hurt, my head aches and I'd appreciate it if you'd just go away. I don't want to hear about the fire and I don't want to hear about Brad's lot that's for sale. Go buy your damned lot from McClatchy and crow over what you've won and leave me alone." Chalcie wasn't in the mood to listen to him.

"Actually, I didn't follow you out here to talk about land." Jordan looked for all the world like a small boy caught stealing a pie off the windowsill. His hands beat a nervous tattoo on his thighs, and he couldn't seem to get a full sentence out.

Chalcie turned to stalk away. Jordan reached out, catch-ing her by the elbow and breaking all the rules of etiquette, to bring her back to him.

His touch burned, and it wasn't just the heat of the day.

"Get your hands off me," Chalcie ground out. Touch her, would he? "If my hands didn't hurt so much, I'd lay you flat on the ground for that, and don't you ever think I couldn't do it!" She refused to acknowledge that she liked to have him close to her and that her heart beat faster when he was near.

Jordan caught her hands and turned them over, wincing at the sight of the burned flesh across the palms. He ran a finger gently along the side of the burns, flinching as the rough flesh pulled under his grasp.

He already felt miserable, this just made it worse. How could he have been such a fool? He knew her better than that. They'd been business rivals for a year, and in all that time he'd never seen her do or say anything that hadn't been the very model of propriety—except when she broke into his house. And last night he had lost his temper in the heat of the moment—he hated himself for it now.

"God, I'm so sorry," he said, looking down at her hands.

"What for? You didn't burn me." She shrugged.

"No, but you got those burns saving my place from going up in flames."

There, it was out. He'd said it.

Jordan couldn't even begin to put into words how he had felt when those men were dragged in, still blinking and half-asleep. They'd been convinced to tell the truth and had confessed to starting the fire to get even with him.

Jordan tried again. "I know I can't call back what I said or thought last night, but I'd like to apologize." From the look on Chalcie's face, she wasn't going to be receptive to his words. Her chin stuck out and her mouth was set in a stubborn, uncompromising line. He faltered and then lapsed into an embarrassed silence. He didn't seem to be making his point too well.

Chalcie looked at Jordan steadily. Let him sweat, she thought. It served him right. Let him think about how he had treated her. Maybe next time he'd keep that temper in check and ask a few questions first.

Jordan looked away, into the kitchen of the bakery, and suddenly he saw a way to make his apology more tangible.

"I'd like to send over some men to help you clean up the bakery and take care of anything else that you need done," he offered, looking at the pans that were piled high, still unwashed from the morning bread.

Chalcie shook her head.

Jordan's fragile hold on his temper snapped. He was trying to do the right thing for her, and she was refusing him even that small solace.

"Chalcie, don't be such a pigheaded fool," Jordan said. "You know it's my fault that you're burned and you need the help. At least let me make amends."

"And you're going to make me feel better by calling me pigheaded? Why, I can't believe that such a compliment came out of your mouth!"

Jordan took off his hat and ran his hand through his hair in exasperation. What was it about this woman that seemed to drive him to distraction? That red hair and those blue eyes, and the way she held her own—Chalcie was unlike any other woman he'd ever met. Of course he'd never betrayed even the slightest weakness where she was concerned. Chalcie would have simply taken the weakness and used it against him.

"Then stop fighting me when I try and help. I don't have a whole lot of patience, as you might have gathered," Jordan said.

"Most men don't. Most men just do whatever they want and then leave it to the women to pick up the pieces," Chalcie replied tartly, thinking that both Jordan and her father had the same approach to women and life in general.

"I'll have the men over here in a few minutes." Jordan looked at her, still trying to figure out the effect that she had on him.

Chalcie thought about refusing him, and then she looked in the back door of the bakery and wilted. All those pans, and her hands ached like fury. She couldn't wash up, she couldn't set the sponge or knead the bread. She needed help and if Jordan was willing to offer it after having been such a fool, well, who was she to tell him no?

"Fine, I accept your offer of help."

Jordan relaxed a bit and simply smiled at her.

"Now, don't you forget, if you need anything else, anything at all, you just ask me. I can't promise that I'll be able to deliver, but I'll give it the best shot I can."

He lifted his hat in a mock salute, placed it on his head again, turned and walked away from Chalcie. His stride was jaunty, as if he'd just come out the victor in a battle.

Chalcie stared after him and didn't know whether to laugh or cry.

Chapter Four

Chalcie had never really noticed before that the two blankets that served as her mattress did nothing to cushion the boards that were the base of her bed. She turned again, hoping to find a place where her hipbone didn't connect with an unyielding surface. Tonight of all nights, when she just wanted to sleep, she couldn't make her thoughts behave. Jordan, her father, gold, land, Pete Ames, fire and sheer desperation all churned through her mind. She was so exhausted she could do nothing but stare into the darkness.

Chalcie sat up and rubbed another ounce of ointment into her skin. She had received a package from Jordan de Chatain containing a sweet-smelling unguent. The package was red and marked with Chinese lettering, so it was a fair bet that it had come from Johnny Tong's shop. The cream had already taken most of the sting out of the palms of her hands. Already she could see that the blisters were drying up, and the skin was more supple.

One of these days, Chalcie thought sleepily, she was going to have to meet Johnny Tong. The man was famous from one end of the gold country to the other as a purveyor of powders, potions and curative herbs.

Chalcie thought it was a shame that Johnny couldn't whip up something that would make her life easier. Something to take away the worry. Something—the thought popped unbidden into her head—to make Jordan de Chatain notice her as a woman.

"Now *that's* ridiculous," Chalcie muttered, realizing just how tired she must have been to think such thoughts.

There wasn't a nostrum in Tong's pharmacopoeia that would make Brad accept partial payment from her when he could get the whole amount, cash in hand, from Jordan de Chatain. There weren't any herbs that would cause her father to think of her as a partner. And certainly there wouldn't be anything she could buy from Mr. Tong that could make Jordan de Chatain find her attractive!

"I've got about the same chance of making Jordan de Chatain do what I ask as I have of digging straight down and finding the mother lode under my bed!" Chalcie muttered.

Finally, she drifted off to sleep. Her last thoughts were of Jordan de Chatain, and those thoughts continued in her dreams.

In the dream, she was dressed in a fine outfit, all pink and white and clean. The dress was a confection of lace and ruffles, and she wore fine, delicate black leather shoes. She was clean, fresh from a bath and shampoo that had lasted for hours. She looked good and she smelled good and even her hair was under control instead of being pulled back into an untidy mop.

Chalcie stepped daintily through the street, careful not to let her dress get soiled before she saw the man she was to marry. She stopped in front of Jordan's house.

Jordan was waiting for her. He put out his hand and welcomed her to his home.

"Are you happy with the bargain?" he asked her. His handsome face was somber. There were no smiles and laughter, no gentle teasing this time.

"I am happy," Chalcie answered simply.

"Then you will become my wife in exchange for the deed to the land?" Jordan asked, still not smiling. His dark hair glowed in the reflected light of the moon, and his eyes were black as night. He reached for her and she stepped forward into his embrace.

As he touched her, she shuddered at the physical impact of his hand against her arm. If this was fire, she burned for him. She wanted to touch him and the clothes were getting in the way. She could feel his body against hers, but there were buttons and a vest and pants with even more buttons, and she was stopped almost before she could start.

Jordan kissed her, and she responded with tenderness, her lips soft against his. Her fingers pulled at the back of his vest and beneath it, against the fine cotton of his shirt. Somewhere under all that cloth, she was certain, there was a real man of flesh and blood. All she had to do was find him. Jordan was driving her mad with the pressure of his lips and the softness of his hands on her neck and her back.

Didn't he want her undressed? Didn't he burn with fire to feel flesh against flesh? She wanted to touch him and taste him, make passionate love to him. She hated the dress that constrained her and she knew that this wild desire, the craving she felt, had gone far beyond a simple bargain. The thrill had nothing to do with auctioning herself off to the highest bidder to retain rights to a piece of land. Jordan had, somehow, broken through her reserve and her distrust.

Chalcie wanted him. She hungered for him and she would have him. Her fingers fought against the shirt, and then, finally, mercifully, it was free. She began to work on the buttons of the pants, her hands between them, feeling every inch of his body. He wanted her, she knew he did, she could feel it, and the heat rose and rose, and she was smothering with desire....

Chalcie awoke and sat upright in bed. She was sweating from the heat. She had the blanket clutched in her hand, her fingers trying to make holes through the worn material. She looked down and blushed. She let the blanket drop, aware of the pain that rubbing the burned skin had caused.

The pain brought her thumping back to the reality of her own bed in her own room.

That dream—she had been trying to unbutton Jordan de Chatain's pants! The very thought made her giddy with disbelief.

How could her mind have tricked her? She didn't love him, she didn't lust after him, she didn't even like him!

Marry Jordan de Chatain?

Of all the men she had ever known, he was the last person she would think of marrying. It would never happen, no matter how handsome he was. That slightly provocative smile had been turned to his advantage with women too many times for her to fall for the same sweet talk. He might be able to sweep other ladies away, but not her. She wasn't vulnerable to his charms—particularly since he was unreasonable, nasty-tempered and greedy when he dealt with her!

Since it was obvious that she wasn't ever going to commit matrimony with Jordan, she knew there had to be a hidden message in the vision. Her mind had been trying to tell her something other than that she should marry Jordan de Chatain—but what was it?

She had learned to count on dreams as a source of some of her best ideas, if she could only unravel them and she was certain that this dream hadn't been a message to make men's pants without buttons so lovemaking would be easier. There was another idea buried in it that she could use. She knew it was there, itching to be found. She twisted and turned the puzzle until she hit on what seemed to be the right combination.

The secret was in the idea of auctioning herself off to the highest bidder. Jordan had already shown that he could be gentle with her, and she couldn't believe that his kindness had been nothing more than that. He had mentioned something about hitting a man who had dared to say something about their supposed relationship, so that meant he cared for her, didn't it? And he had been so kind to her when he had discovered her in his house. Maybe he really did like her but just didn't want to show it.

She had been very much aware of the way Jordan had looked at her, the way he had touched her when they were together. Even if it had been only to help soothe her battered nose, he had been gentle with her. Could it be that he wasn't quite as immune to her charms as he pretended to be?

Perhaps the dream had been trying to tell her she might be able to lead Jordan on. She could tell him she was willing to allow him to court her. She could even talk about marriage. Then, once she had gained his confidence, she could kiss him. At that point she was certain she could convince him to buy the land and then let her buy it from him, or loan her the money to buy it and she could repay him.

After all, hadn't he said he would help her if he could? Well then, he'd hardly be able to refuse an offer that would net him a marriageable woman and release him from the feeling that he'd been unfair to her.

She didn't actually have to marry him or even become engaged to him. One evening would suffice. But Mr. de Chatain wouldn't know that. He'd think that she was genuinely attracted to him. When she had her land, he would be no worse off than he was right now, since he didn't care a fig about her, and she'd be a little richer and a lot safer.

What she was planning wasn't exactly fair, and her conscience would pain her, but it wouldn't be so painful that she couldn't live with it. She'd have the land to soothe her. She chose to ignore the passions that had surfaced in the dream. After all, that had been nighttime fantasy, this was daytime reality.

Chalcie smiled in the darkness. She wouldn't be able to have the pink-and-white dress or the fine shoes of her dreams. Still, given a little time, she and Juanita could come up with a respectably pretty dress. It would be enough to bring Jordan to her side.

She managed to fall asleep again, dreaming about the way she was going to trick Jordan de Chatain.

The next morning she broached the idea to Juanita, explaining in painful detail why and how she intended to catch Jordan de Chatain long enough to win the land. "So you see, Juanita, I need help borrowing a dress or converting something I already have into a dress that will sweep Mr. de Chatain off his feet."

Juanita sat back in the rocking chair and stared at Chalcie. She had listened intently to what Chalcie was saying, her dark face frowning as she followed the plan.

"I think you are a fool to try," Juanita stated.

"What? How can you say such a thing? Don't you understand, I have to save that land...."

Juanita held up her hand to stop Chalcie. "I understand and I also think that Ames is kin to pond slime. But I don't think that Jordan de Chatain is going to be nearly as easy to ensnare as you think."

Chalcie's full lips thinned in a grimace. She didn't want to hear all the reasons why Juanita didn't think it would work; she just wanted Juanita to make her presentable.

Juanita saw her friend's expression and sighed. She stood up and motioned for Chalcie to join her. Juanita's pretty, heart-shaped face was a study in conflicting emotions. She didn't like what Chalcie was going to do, but she hated to turn down a challenge. And the idea of turning this sun-baked hoyden into a real lady by artifices such as a beautiful dress and stylish hair intrigued her.

Juanita thought about her own Miguel and the beautiful lace dress she had worn at their wedding. She still cherished it and wished that Chalcie could have the kind of love that Juanita had already experienced. But it wouldn't happen, at least not with Jordan de Chatain. Juanita put aside the thoughts of Miguel. She had to think of Chalcie, not of the man she missed so much that her heart broke every time she said his name. She was to be a widow the rest of her life, no matter what Eduardo said. He could come to court her and drink one whiskey and make it last all night, just to look at her, but she had been hurt once. Death had taken her perfect mate and she wasn't going to try to love another man.

Ah, but Eduardo...

Juanita refused to think of him, either. She had work to do in transforming Chalcie into the beauty she was underneath the tough exterior. A bath, a nice dress and brushed hair might actually make her look like a lady.

"All right, since you're determined to do this thing, show me what you have in the trunk. We'll see what can be worked out."

The trunk, however, held no treasures. Chalcie had her one hated pink cotton dress that she was wearing, and one old cotton work dress that should have been cut up for rags long ago. She had a fine velvet dress for trips into San Francisco, but the thought of wearing the heavy garment in the heat and dust of a Sonora summer was ludicrous. The only other clothes she possessed were a fancy white cotton bodice with lace and ribbon and a flounced underskirt of the same material.

"And you have nothing else? Nothing at all that we could use to make a dress?" Juanita demanded in horror. She had never guessed that her boss, the woman who was responsible for the Kent fortunes, might not have a whole wardrobe of beautiful things tucked away in her tiny bedroom.

Chalcie shrugged helplessly. "I guess I could try and borrow something...."

"What do you have in the store? Tell me, do you not have at least one bolt of cloth in that place?" Juanita's dark brown eyes were lit with fire. She wasn't going to give up on this.

"Nothing," Chalcie said. Well, not exactly nothing, but she couldn't imagine wearing a dress made of the heavy red flannel that she did have for sale.

"Let me think…" Juanita said, putting her hand to her mouth.

"I could borrow something," Chalcie suggested again, though she didn't know from whom she might borrow. The only woman who was near her size was Juanita, and she was certain Juanita had no more clothes than she did.

"From whom?" Juanita asked sharply.

Chalcie shrugged, beginning to lose hope.

Then she thought of the traveling salesman who'd passed through town in the spring. He had brought with him an astounding variety of useless objects. Someone in San Francisco had told him that the men in the gold country were desperate enough to buy anything with their newfound wealth, and he had believed them. He had for sale fancy Spanish combs, cast-iron tea kettles and a vest of silk and velvet. The men had laughed at him, passing over his goods for those of the next drummer who had followed on his heels with good solid boots and sturdy gloves among his wares. The first drummer had moved on, leaving his worthless fripperies, as well as a pile of fine linen tablecloths, for Chalcie to sell if she could. He had told her he would be back sometime during the year and she could give him whatever she felt was fair if she sold any of the goods.

"Would white linen do?" Chalcie asked.

"Certainly, if there was any available in this godforsaken country. But there isn't. Where are you going to find something like that here?" Juanita asked.

"Follow me!" Chalcie led the way out into the street and down to the store.

She barely noticed when Eduardo, the young man who was smitten with Juanita, called out a greeting. Juanita, however, waved shyly and was excruciatingly aware of Eduardo's eyes on her as she hurried behind Chalcie.

Inside it was cool and dim, a wonderful contrast to the heat outside. Chalcie reached beneath the counter and picked up the linen cloths. Both Chalcie and Juanita examined the designs that had been hand stitched around the borders. There were leaves and roses, tiny daisies and whole sheaves of irises on the various tablecloths. Some of them sported delicate lace cutouts and others fine-colored thread and stuffed designs that made them stand out in relief against the plain linen.

"Here, this is the one we'll use for the top. It'll be cut plain, with a square neck and long sleeves, but with an opening up the whole of the sleeve so you won't die of the heat." Juanita pulled out a cream-colored tablecloth that was embroidered with delicate white baby roses. The embroidery had been done in the barest, most delicate shade of rose, and Juanita knew that the color would make Chalcie bloom. She could see how to cut the cloth to use the most of the borders. When she finished with the sewing and fitting, the dress would be the talk of the town. And with Chalcie's tanned complexion and red hair brushed and burnished and curled, she would be stunningly beautiful. Despite her misgivings, Juanita was beginning to get excited about the whole idea.

"Let's use this one for the bottom. Look at this border, all dark brown embroidered and cut lace! No one will be able to say it isn't the prettiest dress they've ever seen," Chalcie crowed. She could see it now. Jordan de Chatain would never have a chance! He'd see her in the dress, all clean and sweet smelling, and he'd be more than happy to give her anything she wanted.

The next two days were spent in a marathon sewing bee. Chalcie hadn't worked so hard since she turned out all those uniforms to save her father's hide from the Mexican army. Her hands ached and burned, and she sometimes had to stop short and cry with the pain of holding the needle. But she kept on in spite of it. She had only three days to make her idea work. She had to convince Jordan that courting her was a good idea, get the assignment of the land and have the papers signed in the next three days. When it was finished, she'd be safe, no matter what her father did when he came down from the mountains.

"I wish you'd think about what you're doing," Juanita fretted. "I don't want you to get hurt. He's been known to break a few hearts. Besides, you're not exactly being fair with him."

"I'm not doing this because I think I'm going to fall in love with him. I'm just going to...use...him." Chalcie thought carefully about the words.

"Watch out," Juanita tried again to caution her. "I don't think he'd ever let anyone use him in his life. I'd hate to see you get hurt," she said again, though she hated to belabor the point.

Chalcie didn't want to argue. Nothing was going to deter her from her plan. Besides, Juanita didn't know anything about Jordan's offer to help her.

Instead, they talked about Juanita and what her life had been like back in Jalisco, when she and Miguel were courting.

"It was so different, so beautiful. The romance could be felt in the very air. At home, we never met each other except in a group and with adults always present. Our courting took place at dances, with stolen kisses." Juanita's hands stopped stitching for a moment as the repressed memories flooded back. It hurt, but she wanted so much to talk about Miguel that she would brave the pain.

"The men dressed in white and the women wore their fanciest embroidered blouses and skirts and *rebozos*." She stopped for a moment, trying to think of the American word, and then remembered. "*Rebozos* are shawls, some of them very intricate and beautiful. If you are rich, they are woven with gold in the cloth. I had nothing so fancy, only a white one that I had embroidered with red, orange and blue flowers and lovely leaves...." She had left it behind when she came to California with Miguel. There had been no place in the small satchels they had carried when they set out for the gold fields. She hoped that one of her sisters was using the *rebozo* to entice her own man into proposing marriage.

"The dances?" Chalcie prodded her. She was fascinated by the life that Juanita had lived before coming to Sonora.

"The most popular dance was the hat dance, because at the end, the men would take off their hats and put them to the side of their face, hiding them from onlookers. The women would dance in close, and there would be time for one stolen kiss." Her eyes misted with tears. How sweet those kisses had been. She would have given anything for another touch of Miguel's lips to hers.

"It sounds wonderful," Chalcie sighed. "So romantic, and nothing at all like what I'm trying to do with Jordan."

"No, nothing at all the same," Juanita said, and picked up the needle again. Chalcie had to want love and romance first, and there had never been any indication to Juanita that Chalcie craved romance nearly as much as she wanted riches and land. She stitched down the seam and started another one. There was so much sewing to finish and very little time to accomplish everything that had to be done.

Juanita would have liked to talk to Chalcie about Eduardo, but she was too shy to reveal her thoughts on the man. Still, she couldn't get him out of her mind. He was a kind, gentle man, even good-looking, but he frightened her. She had no wish to fall in love again, yet it seemed to be happening in spite of herself. He was careful with his gold, didn't waste it on drink—or on the women in town. She liked him, but she didn't love him. She was certain of that.

Chalcie and Juanita took turns sewing and tending the bar until late into the night. Finally Chalcie made the last stitch on the skirt. She broke the thread and stored the needle carefully away in her trunk. She swept her hand over the cool cream of the linen, marveling at the beautiful dress that the tablecloths had made. When the drummer came back she would have to give him double his price for having left her the means to entice Jórdan de Chatain into her little trap.

The next day Chalcie and Juanita trudged up the hill to the small lake that had been formed in one of the ground depressions and been widened by several of the men for use in their mining. Chalcie paid five dollars in gold for the privilege of taking a bath in the pool. Juanita stood guard with a rifle, and Chalcie bathed while still wearing all her clothes. By the time she had finished, she had lathered and soaped and splashed enough that she was chilled through and felt marvelously clean. She wrapped a blanket around her to shield her body from the stares of the men.

Once in her room she stripped and put on the lacy bodice and underskirt.

"Let me fix your hair now, before you dress any further. Otherwise, it's going to dry into a mass of curls that we'll never get untangled." Juanita made Chalcie sit on the edge of the bed while she plied the silver brush and comb. She used several of her own pins for Chalcedony's hair and bent and twisted the rebellious red mass into a glowing crown of curls. It would be fine if Chalcie remembered to move like a lady and not a rambunctious mule, she thought.

"Now, the dress…"

Chalcie obediently stood and picked up the white linen confection that awaited her. It wasn't at all the pink lace and frills that she had so loved in the dream, but it was still beautiful.

She pulled the skirt over her hips, preferring to fight with the underskirt rather than have her hair messed by the material catching and tearing out the curls. She fastened the skirt at the waist with silken ties that had also been contained in the peddler's pack. The skirt fitted beautifully, extending just to the top of her old work boots, the flounce with the dark brown embroidery looking as if it had never been anything else except the elegant skirt.

Next the blouse. Chalcie put it on and then looked up at Juanita in alarm.

"Don't you think this is just a little bit too low?" she asked, tugging at the neckline as if she could somehow adjust it up to her neck instead of the spot where Jordan might be able to see something of the tops of her breasts. She hadn't meant to be quite so exposed.

"Stop pulling at it!" Juanita slapped her hands away. "You're going to rip the stitches loose, and it looks just fine the way it is. Now, turn around and let me fasten the back and the cuffs."

They were both proud of the buttons they had found. One of the miners had discarded a dress shirt that he had no use for, and Chalcie and Juanita had pounced on the piece of cloth, stripping the buttons from it before the miner could object. Chalcie was especially glad to have the ivory buttons, since she had been prepared to carve her own small fastenings from a piece of manzanita bush. The dark red would have looked fine, but the real buttons were better.

Juanita stood back and then frowned.

"Is something wrong? Did we cut it wrong?" Chalcie saw the expression on Juanita's face and panicked. She didn't need anything to go wrong at the last minute.

"It's the boots. I'm sorry, Chalcie, but we've got to find something else for you to wear. You just can't go out in an elegant gown with your hair up in curls and wearing dirty, heavy old mining boots. It just won't do."

Chalcie looked down at her feet and almost cried. She had forgotten that she was wearing the boots. They went on her feet first thing in the morning and came off last thing at night, and she never even gave them a thought. The boots protected her feet from gashes and bruises and that was all she expected them to do. They had never had pretensions of being the sleek black leather fancy shoes of her dream. They were also the only footwear she owned.

Silently Chalcie turned around and let Juanita unfasten the dress. It fitted and she looked good, but they had finally run into the one thing she couldn't change. She could do nothing about her shoes, and the idea of going to Jordan barefoot or with heavy boots on didn't even deserve to be thought about.

Chalcie put on her now dry pink cotton dress and let

Juanita remove the pins from her hair. It fell to her shoulders, a magnificent fall of golden red.

"Well, we tried," Chalcie said helplessly.

She spent the afternoon in the store, thinking about shoes. By the end of the day she was near tears from frustration.

"Please?" a small voice called her from the back of the store. Chalcie whipped around, startled at the sound.

"Please, could you help?" A very old Chinese gentleman stood at the back door, resting heavily on the black carved cane that he held. He dared not come to the front of the store—Chinese were not even allowed in this part of town, but he needed one ingredient for his potions and he had heard from several people that only Chalcie was likely to carry it.

Chalcie motioned for him to come into the store. The old man hesitated and then sidled in, obviously uncomfortable in the white man's store.

"Please, do you have red pepper spices? Hot? Perhaps your Juanita would have them?" He looked at her hopefully. His hand shook on the cane, and it was obvious from the paleness of his face that he was frightened at his own boldness in coming to see Chalcie.

"Red pepper? Yes, I have some. But it's dried and on a string—is that what you want?" Chalcie asked uncertainly. She reached to one side of the counter, where the peppers had been languishing since she bought them two months ago. No one except Juanita had been interested in the spice once they had tasted the fiery fruits. One bite was enough to ensure tears, swearing and a general rebellion among miners, so the cooks had stayed away from the little red bundles and substituted milder spices for the meals that were cooked in boardinghouses and over heated coals outside. That left Chalcie with the red peppers, and Juanita couldn't eat the whole five-foot length of them.

"Oh, that is perfect," the man said softly. He caressed the peppers, sniffed them and even took a small bite to see that they were what he was seeking. He rolled the bite around in his mouth, obviously savoring the oils that had threatened to burn the miners' throats. Not even a tear appeared in his eyes. It was obvious that he was used to such things and Chalcie regarded him in admiration and a little awe. She had never been able to stand more than the smell of the chilies.

Then it struck her—this was Johnny Tong! That was why he needed the chilies. He could use them in his special potions that were to cure or calm, or induce love. He wasn't about to waste them on cooking!

"Mr. Tong?"

The man looked at her in surprise. Few of the Americans knew his name.

"Yes?"

"Mr. Tong, look." Chalcie held out her hands, palm up, so he could see the burns that were healing faster than she had thought possible.

"Ah, you are the one with the burn." Mr. Tong bowed gently to her. He had a faint smile, as if he were glad to see that the medication had worked as he had expected it would.

"Yes, I'm the one with the burn, and thank you for the cream. If I hadn't had it, I would have sat in a corner and cried with the pain."

Mr. Tong looked at her thoughtfully and then shook his head.

"No, you would not cry. You would fight through the pain, and it would make you weak and sick. Don't always be fighting, child. One of these days you'll give up the fight and you'll come to me for herbs to bring on love and I will help you," Mr. Tong said gently.

Chalcie's eyes widened. She had never heard anything so silly in her life. She didn't always fight...and what would he know about it, anyway? And a love potion? No, that was for the women who worked in the second-story fandango parlors, not for Chalcedony Kent.

"Here, take these," Chalcie said, shoving the peppers into Mr. Tong's hands. She looked down, trying to avoid his curious stare. She realized as she stared at his feet that Mr. Tong was wearing the answer to all her problems. His feet were encased in slippers of black, with just a bit of gold embroidery on the toes. They were delicate compared to the heavy boots worn by the miners and Chalcie. She had never seen anything like them. She would pay almost anything for those shoes; they would be perfect with her dress.

"How much, please?" Mr. Tong held up the string of peppers.

"One pair of shoes," Chalcie answered quickly.

Mr. Tong began to lay the peppers back on the table regretfully. He had not expected this woman to make fun of him after his burn cream had worked so well for her. But by now he was beginning to know that the white people would go to almost any lengths to make a Chinese man feel uncomfortable. He should have anticipated that Chalcie would be the same way.

"So sorry to have bothered you." He turned and started out the back door.

"But I thought you wanted them?" Chalcie was bewildered.

"I do. But not at the price of having a joke made at me."

"No, please, you don't understand," Chalcie said. "I wasn't making fun of you. I really want a pair of shoes like the ones you are wearing, unless you feel that the price is too high...." She forced the last words out. She had no idea what such a pair of shoes cost, but if they were terribly expensive, she'd have to do without them.

"You truly want these as payment?" Mr. Tong stared at her, his wrinkled old face a study in perplexity. He was still trying to fathom the inscrutable white woman's mind. What would a woman like Chalcie do with a pair of men's shoes? "These are not too expensive. Probably peppers are worth more."

"I don't care. I want a pair just like those, if possible. I'll even take the ones that you're wearing." Chalcie was getting desperate.

"Please, take a piece of paper and draw around your foot. I will endeavor to have a pair of shoes that will be comfortable for you before the evening is over. New shoes, not used ones," Mr. Tong said. "I will send boy with shoes, and you may give him the peppers."

"Take the peppers. I trust you. But please, send the shoes as fast as you can. I need them!"

Chalcie found a piece of paper, removed one of her heavy boots and drew around her right foot, bending awkwardly to reach behind her heel. She handed the man the outline and the chilies and sent up a fervent prayer that he would actually keep his promise.

As soon as he left, she closed the door of the shop and ran to the bar. She pulled Juanita aside and told her of the shoes that were to be delivered.

"Once the shoes are here, I can go find Mr. de Chatain and make him the offer. Isn't it wonderful? It has to be an omen. Everything is working out even when I had no right to expect it," Chalcie crowed.

She'd have the land before the next day was over, she was certain.

Chapter Five

"All right, I have it set up with French Jeannie and Cross Leg Sadie," Juanita said as she hurried into the back of the bar to take over again from Chalcie. "Sadie's going to see that de Chatain is outside the fandango parlor when the moon rises over the top of the mountains." Juanita watched Chalcie's hands tremble as she poured the whiskey into the glasses. She wasn't the least bit sympathetic with Chalcie's last-minute nerves. She shouldn't have been trying to cheat Jordan by promising something that she had no intention of delivering.

"Sadie won't promise that he'll stay out there long, but she's told him that there is someone who wants to meet him."

Juanita took the filled glasses from Chalcie and set them before the miners. She smiled briefly at Eduardo but didn't offer him another drink. Juanita knew he would stay with the one glass of whiskey, sipping it and staring at her for the rest of the night.

"That gives us about an hour to get you ready. And look at your hair, you've let it get tangled again," Juanita said, gazing at what used to be a perfect fall of red curls.

"Couldn't help it. I had cleaning up at the store to do," Chalcie said. "I figured that as long as I had to wait around for the shoes, I'd better make use of the time."

"Couldn't you have taken care of the books? At least then your hair wouldn't look like a mouse's nest. You actually ought to take another bath, and now there isn't time!" Juanita frowned at Chalcie.

"Don't fret. I'll wash off and everything, even my hair, will be fine. The shoes are beautiful. I don't know how Johnny Tong knew what I needed them for, but he sent dark brown shoes, almost exactly the shade of the embroidery on the dress. They have just a little gold on them, but they are perfect for tonight."

"Luck, that's what it is. I've never seen such a run of luck, not even at the gambling tables. Maybe you are right. Maybe you were meant to go meet Jordan de Chatain tonight," Juanita said. "Now go on home and I'll meet you there in a couple of minutes."

Chalcie grabbed one of the tin can lights on her way out and walked the length of the building. She lifted the calico curtain and stepped inside. The skirt and blouse were just where she had left them, with the small brown cloth shoes resting on the trunk beside the skirt. She stripped and then pulled on the skirt and tied the waist. Her fingers were awkward, but the burn didn't pull quite as badly after she applied more unguent. She sat on the side of the bed to slip on the shoes, which were soft, with a thin sole of some pliant padded material. They were comfortable and light, and her toes felt cool in them. She stepped around the room and her feet almost begged her to dance. She took a few steps and almost collided with Juanita as she lifted the curtain.

"My, don't you look fine," she said, laughing. Chalcie's hair was still a mess and her face was pink with excitement. There was a gleam in her eyes that certainly hadn't been put there by romance, Juanita knew. Even in the lovely skirt, Chalcie still looked like the untamed hellion she really was.

"Put on the top and I'll fasten it for you, and we'll work on your hair," Juanita said briskly.

They were done well within the hour allotted, and this time when Chalcie stood in front of Juanita, the effect was almost breathtaking. The curls were softer and there were wisps of red hair that strayed around her face and her neck despite Juanita's best efforts. The blouse was still crisp, but this time Chalcie was comfortable with the neckline and the way the arms opened almost to the shoulder in a teasing dance of cloth and flesh. The brown Chinese slippers were perfect, just as Chalcie had said.

If Jordan didn't succumb to this vision, he would have to be the most hard-hearted, unromantic soul in the entire West.

Juanita ducked outside and looked at the mountains. There, just above the ridge, the moon was appearing. It was time for Chalcie to go meet Jordan. For a moment Juanita almost forgot that it was greed, not romance, that was causing this beautiful young woman to go out in the middle of the night to meet a man.

"What a shame," she murmured, then lifted the curtain even further so Chalcie could step out onto the six boards that served as the sidewalk and front porch of her quarters.

"Good luck," Juanita said.

"I could wish you the same. I'm only going to Mr. de Chatain for money. At least you could meet with Eduardo for love…it's not a bad thing, you know," Chalcie said.

"Love isn't a part of my life now. He's very nice, but—"

"I know, he's not your Miguel. But oh, Juanita, no one is ever going to be your Miguel. Give the man a chance."

"Maybe later," Juanita replied reluctantly. And here she'd thought that Chalcie hadn't even seen Eduardo. "Now hurry up, it's getting late." She motioned for Chalcie to stop procrastinating and get on with her plan.

Juanita hurried back toward the bar at the C. K. Saloon. She had no words of wisdom that Chalcie hadn't already heard and ignored.

Chalcie knew exactly where she would be meeting Jordan, but as she approached the back of his fandango parlor, she didn't see anyone waiting for her. As she walked toward the darkness at the back of the building, her pulse began to race with excitement and just a little worry. But she was only doing what Jordan had suggested when he apologized for accusing her of setting the fire.

Jordan had told her to tell him if there was anything he could do for her. Well, here was his chance to live up to his word. She needed that land and he could help her get it. She slowed and then almost stopped. She knew he had meant what he said, but had he meant to give away land? She didn't think so. Besides, she wasn't being honorable herself. She would only be offering him something she had no intention of delivering—herself. The little lie would help both of them. Jordan would be free of his obligation to her after his tirade about the fire, and Chalcie would have her land in her own name.

Chalcie ignored the fact that the deceit made her conscience prickle.

Jordan stood in the shadows and watched as Chalcie picked her way carefully between the rocks and bits of debris that cluttered the area behind the saloons and fandango parlors. He had been struck first by the thought of how beautiful she looked, far more beautiful than he would ever have guessed the half-wild, rapacious Chalcie that he knew could ever have been. Even the glimpse he'd had of the woman beneath the man's clothing when she had come to see the cat hadn't hinted at this beauty. He was also intrigued by the fact that she was the person who wanted to meet him.

In the hours since French Jeannie had told him there was someone who wanted to see him behind the fandango parlor to talk to him, he had wondered who it was. He had even taken his knife and slipped it into his waistband, ready to be thrown at an instant's notice. He had thought about who could want to talk to him and who wanted revenge. Never, in his wildest imaginings, had he come up with

Chalcie. She had no reason to seek him out. In fact, since the confrontation several days ago, he hadn't expected her to be interested in seeing him ever again.

He still felt bad about the way he'd attacked her for something she didn't do, but he'd tried to make amends for that. Surely she couldn't still be angry with him for that trouble? He touched the knife. He hoped she wasn't still angry with him.

Chalcie had walked steadily toward him, and he had inched back into the shadows to study her before he acknowledged her presence. She looked more beautiful than he had ever seen her, and he could only shake his head in wonderment. Those eyes haunted him as he remembered the pain and despair he had seen in them the night he had found her in his house. There was something about her mouth that made him want to kiss her to see if she tasted as sweet as she looked. He was immediately aware of a slight tightening as he remembered just how fine she had felt when he caught her after she ran head-on into his chest; she had been warm and soft. There had been a magic there that he didn't even want to think about. Becoming interested in Chalcedony Kent could only lead to trouble.

What the hell am I thinking? he chastised himself. He didn't even like her. The only reason he'd offered his help if she ever needed it was because he knew he'd acted rashly when he'd foolishly accused her of any wrongdoing.

The same question came back as he looked at her. What could the woman want?

Chalcie hesitated and looked around. She still didn't see Jordan. She bit her lip, wondering if she should peek into the parlor, or just turn around and go back home. The moon was well beyond the mountain now, and, if Jordan didn't appear within a very few minutes, she was going to head back to her own place. A lone woman, however well known, wasn't really safe on the streets of Sonora at this time of night. She knew, too, that in her new dress and fancy hairdo, she didn't look like the Chalcie Kent everyone knew, and that in itself could place her in danger if a drunken miner happened to spy her and take a liking to her feminine form.

Finally, his curiosity got the better of him, and Jordan stepped forward.

"Hello, Chalcie. Are you looking for me?"

Jordan's voice and sudden appearance not more than three feet in front of her startled Chalcie so much she jumped and almost fell as her ankle connected with part of a broken barrel.

Jordan moved swiftly, catching her before she could fall and ruin her dress. His arms closed around her, and, for a breathless second they were as close as they had been in her dream. Jordan held her just one moment longer than necessary. She was just as soft and sweet as he remembered.

"Catching you seems to be something of a habit, doesn't it? At least this time there won't be any blood." Jordan began to respond to the soft body in his arms and cursed underneath his breath. He didn't need this complication in his life!

Chalcie looked up at him, wide-eyed. She could feel his breath against her cheek, and she was acutely aware of his lips just inches from her own. The images of the dream came back to her, her eyes widening even further. She sighed involuntarily and then stepped back, freeing herself from his embrace. That damned dream was making her think like a woman instead of a person with negotiations on her mind. Unbuttoning his pants, indeed! She was there on business, not romance. And she didn't even like the man, she reminded herself.

"Yes, I was looking for you," Chalcie said, aware that her voice was softer than normal. Then she couldn't think of another thing to say. Was she supposed to remind him of his promise? Why hadn't she worked this out? she berated herself. Why hadn't she practiced the speech she would give, so she wouldn't be tongue-tied when she came face-to-face with him?

This wasn't going to work!

"Well? Here I am. I was told you wanted to talk to me." Jordan was looking at her. His face was solemn but there was a glint in his dark eyes that might have signaled the start of laughter.

Chalcie couldn't stand being laughed at, particularly by a man like Jordan de Chatain.

"I wanted to see you and…" Chalcie couldn't force herself to go on. Her hands pleated the side of her dress, permanently creasing the folds of cream linen. Her mind refused to work, and her heart was beating so hard that she couldn't have heard anything Jordan had to say, anyway.

Jordan waited. He looked again at her face and then let his eyes stray just a bit downward, to the gentle swell of her breasts. If he hadn't known better, he would have thought she might be trying to catch his eye. Chalcie Kent, however, had never exhibited the least interest in any of the men in the camp as far as he knew. Until a few nights ago, Chalcie had never been linked romantically with anyone. The miners' rumors about a romance with him had been dreamed up out of nothing more substantial than fairy dust and wishes. Chalcie wasn't interested in anything other than building the Kent empire.

So if the beautiful white dress and the fetchingly arranged hair and the soft voice were all for his benefit, he knew that it had to be about business, not romance.

Suddenly he understood, and cursed himself for being a fool before. The only business they might have in common was the land that was now up for grabs because Brad McClatchy wanted to sell and go back home. She'd even mentioned it when they met outside the bakery.

Jordan felt a slight twinge of regret when he finally figured out what Chalcie was doing. It might have been fun, he thought, if she had been interested in seeing him so-

cially. Wouldn't their courting have given the town something to talk about!

Jordan nodded. "I think I know what this is all about.
We both have an interest in the land that Brad offered to
you."

Chalcie sighed in relief. At least he was helping her by
giving her the opening she needed.

She nodded. "I need to ask a favor of you."

Jordan raised one eyebrow. He stared at her, momentari-
ly distracted by the sight of her; she was magnificent. He
wanted to reach out and touch her hair, then taste her lips.
He wanted, in a word, to make love to her.

Jordan shook his head to clear it. He'd been standing
around the whiskey barrel too long and the fumes were
obviously addling his brain. He couldn't allow himself to
be fascinated by the face and the hair and the low-cut gown,
which gave him just a glimpse of her firm white breasts.
He had to remember that he was dealing with Chalcie Kent,
not one of the tarts in the fandango parlors. She could be
dangerous, they could not. And she wanted to ask a favor
of him.

"Tell me what you want." He couldn't imagine why she
had even come to talk to him about it. She had first choice,
and all she had to do was bring in a paltry two thousand
dollars of gold and the land was hers. She didn't need him
to help with that. And once she had acquired the land, she
certainly wouldn't be dealing with him as anything other
than an adversary when she built whatever it was she'd
decided was needed in the gold town. So far she had done
just fine without his help.

Chalcie took a deep breath.

"I need to have you purchase the land for me and then
let me buy it back from you in two weeks' time, at twenty
percent interest," Chalcie said, her voice still soft and almost romantic.

Jordan stared at her, hardly able to believe his ears. She
wanted him to buy the land and then sell it back to her?

The very land that they'd both been coveting for almost a year? She had to be crazy!

"Not a chance," Jordan said firmly. "When I offered my help, it didn't include cutting my own throat. I need that piece of land just as much as you do."

Oh, no you don't, Chalcie thought bitterly. Jordan de Chatain didn't have a father who was intent on ruining any chance of his financial stability. He had no idea what was at stake for her.

"Please, I need that land!"

"So do I. What gave you the idea that I'd buy it for you and then hand it over for twenty percent profit? If I just hold on to the land for a year, I can probably sell it at one hundred percent profit and not have to deal with you." Jordan could have kicked himself the instant the words were out of his mouth. He hadn't meant to insult her.

Chalcie gasped. "So that's the way you're going to help me when I need it." Chalcie was contemptuous. She'd known all along that Jordan was a liar. He didn't mean it when he offered his assistance, especially if giving it would cost him money.

"That wasn't what I meant," Jordan hastened to assure her.

"Certainly it was. You don't want to help me, and that's all I really need to know. But think for just a moment about what I'm offering. I'll give you thirty percent if you'll help me buy Brad McClatchy's land. It can even be in your name until I pay off the debt."

That way she would be absolutely certain that her father wouldn't know anything at all about the investment. The land would be in Jordan's name, not her own, until after Ames took what he wanted and left.

Jordan shook his head again, and there wasn't a trace of a smile on his handsome face. "Not even for fifty percent interest in two weeks. If you cannot buy the land, then I have plans for it."

Chalcie stood there in an agony of indecision. Should

she go ahead with the second part of her plan or just walk away? She had been such a fool to believe that he had meant it when he'd offered help to her.

But if this didn't work, everything she ever valued in the world—the comfort and the safety of her own home, the solid satisfaction of knowing there would be a meal to eat at the end of the day and fresh bread in the morning, even if she did have to bake it herself—would be taken away from her. She was certain Pete Ames would ruin everything she'd worked so hard for. She had to go through with the second part of the plan.

"Was there something else?" Jordan was all business.

Maybe it wasn't such a good plan, after all. Chalcie was almost ready to turn and walk away from him, until she thought about Pete Ames and her father and the chance that she could be broke and hungry within a few months if she didn't do something to protect herself.

"I could offer you something more valuable than mere money for the chance to buy back the property," Chalcie said, her voice so soft that Jordan almost didn't hear her. Desperation prodded her into action.

"What?"

"I could give you something that most men would fight for the chance to have," Chalcie said. There, she had brought it out in the open. She wasn't going to leave until she had given it her best try.

"And what would that be?" Jordan was smiling now, and his dark eyes glinted with amusement. Chalcie wasn't the type to give anything valuable away. What did she think she could offer him that he would not find worthless?

"Chalcie, I already have saloons, I have fandango parlors and property. I own part interest in producing mines. What more is there besides the land that we both want?"

Chalcie looked at him. She had to say it now or she would lose her nerve.

"I could offer you a chance to court me," Chalcie said.

Jordan stared at her, and then, to Chalcie's amazement, he bit his lips as if he were actually trying not to laugh.

"Court you?"

"Yes, court me. I'd even be willing to consider—after a proper amount of time—uh…marriage." Chalcie's voice was cracking.

"Marriage?" Jordan sounded as if he were strangling on the word.

Chalcie began to think he was not quite as bright as she had thought. "You know what I mean, courting, the same way that men do back in the States when they find a proper, respectable lady that they're attracted to." Chalcie was beginning to lose patience with this man. Was he hard of hearing or just a little dense on the subject of women?

"Of course, if you've been around the girls in the parlors too long, you might have forgotten what keeping company with a decent woman means," Chalcie challenged him.

Jordan laughed then and shook his head. "No, I haven't forgotten what keeping company is all about. But, Chalcie, love and romance haven't had much impact on my life in Sonora, either."

He thought for just a moment about giving in and allowing Chalcie to have the land, free and clear, for a chance to take her as his wife.

But he didn't need a wife, particularly not Chalcedony Kent, who would bring him nothing but trouble. He shuddered to think that if he courted and married her, he'd then be related to James Kent; nothing in the world could convince him that marriage, even to a woman like Chalcie, would be worth such trouble. No matter how alluring she was, they were simply incompatible. Firmly he pushed aside the thought of how good she had felt when he held her.

Chalcie was beginning to get a little nervous. This wasn't the way he was supposed to react. She decided to offer her company to him again, in case he hadn't quite heard her the first time.

"For the chance to buy back that land, with no one knowing the transaction has taken place, I'm willing to offer you the opportunity to court me. I've never allowed anyone else that privilege, though quite a few have asked, as you can imagine." She tried not to sound self-satisfied and failed.

"I'm certain they have, and I admire their choice, but I'm not interested at the moment," Jordan said, and there it was, a slight smile at the edges of his mouth. He was laughing at her!

Chalcie's eyes opened wide, staring at him. "You don't want to keep company?" Her voice sounded like a small child's in the darkness. "But I thought…" She stopped. There was nothing to be said. She had totally misread the way he had looked at her, the way he had touched her. She'd been deluded by her own need to acquire that land— and a few fairy tales she had tried to force herself into believing could come true. He wasn't even interested in her.

She was going to die of shame!

Jordan almost regretted his words. Chalcie was quite a woman. She was luscious, she tempted him, and she had the ability to touch him in a way no other woman ever had. Still, it wasn't enough to make him forget that she was rapacious and tough and that the only reason she wanted to allow him to court her was for the land. Not love, not affection, not even physical attraction. Just money. He'd never paid for love before and he wasn't about to start now, no matter how enticing the prize package was.

Now he had to find a way to allow her to walk away without feeling she had been shamed.

"Chalcie, you are beautiful and desirable and all the things that any man would want. But I don't need a betrothed or a wife right now. I need that land, and if I'm able to buy it, I will."

"Please…" Chalcie was reduced to begging. "Please, I need the land, too."

"Then buy it with gold, or sell one of your other properties. But don't try and buy it with yourself. You're worth much more than a strip of land between our bars.''

Chalcie's eyes were stinging with unshed tears of furious anger.

He had promised! She had saved his damned building and everything else, maybe even the town, and he had promised her that he would do what he could if she ever asked for help. Well, she'd begged him to help her now, and he refused!

The humiliation struck deep and hard. He was turning her down. She couldn't believe it; he was going to buy the land and ignore her offer.

"Right now, I'm worth exactly that strip of land. And if you don't want me, then I shall have to find some other way of stopping you," she threatened in desperation.

"You cannot do it without gold. If you have that gold, you still have until Sunday afternoon to deliver it to Brad McClatchy. Otherwise, Chalcie, the land is mine."

Chalcie turned away blindly. The anger and bitterness were so deep that they burned in her gut as she walked away from him and away from the only chance she would ever have to save herself.

Chapter Six

"Juanita, free drinks for everyone!" Chalcie said as she strode into the C.K. bar.

Juanita looked up and stared at Chalcie. Her face was absolutely white underneath her tan, and her eyes glittered. If Juanita hadn't known better, she would have said that Chalcie looked like a woman with a high fever.

"What did you say?" she asked in disbelief. Chalcie had never given away anything in her life, and here she was, giving away free drinks.

"I said on the house for everyone," Chalcie announced again, and the words were almost drowned out by the roar of approval from the miners. The men were laughing, clapping and stamping in delight. An undertone swept through the room as the men noticed Chalcedony. Most of them had never seen her dressed in anything other than her pink calico dress. They knew she was an attractive woman, but most of them hadn't realized just how beautiful she really was. In the embroidered dress with the low neckline, there was no mistaking the fact that Chalcie was easily the most magnificent woman in Sonora. More than one man's eyes strayed to the revealing bodice and the glorious red crown of hair, and at least twenty men resolved to ask her to marry them, just as soon as they had the chance.

Eduardo leaned close to Juanita and whispered something, and Juanita nodded.

"You're right, there might be trouble. Free drinks and a
beautiful woman can spell a real bad night," Juanita said
as she gratefully accepted Eduardo's help.

"I will protect Chalcie from harm, if necessary, but I am
anxious to make certain that you are safe, Juanita,"
Eduardo said quietly.

Juanita smiled briefly, happy to accept the assistance under any terms. She didn't need anyone to guard her, she
had done just fine since Miguel died, but the men still might
get rough and she didn't want to face them alone.

"Perhaps after this evening is over, we will be able to
spend a few minutes together?" Eduardo asked.

Juanita nodded shyly. Perhaps they could be alone together, after all.

The bartender saw the expressions on the men's faces
and realized that if Chalcie presented herself like this more
often, she could easily outdraw the woman with the veils
and that ridiculous music box. Already more men were
crowding into the saloon as word of the free drinks and
Chalcie's transformation swept through the street.

"Belly up to the bar, men, here we go!" Juanita sang
out. She set up rows of shot glasses and hurried along the
bar pouring, emptying bottles and pouring again. There was
no way to make certain that no one was cheated out of the
free drink; she just kept pouring until the bar's bottles and
kegs were exhausted. Within an hour there were only a few
miners left in Jordan's bar, and a near riot had developed
outside the C. K. Saloon.

A smaller, though more unpleasant, scene threatened to
get out of hand when the supplies started to dwindle.

"What the hell are those two Mexicans doing back there,
anyway? If Juanita's saving the best stuff for her darkie
friends, let's go out back and get into the storage ourselves." Blackie Hardesty's voice rose above the general
roar of the crowd. There was an abortive move toward the

back of the bar. Eduardo stepped forward, and suddenly there was a knife at Blackie Hardesty's throat, just barely pricking the surface.

"Mr. Hardesty, you will not say such a thing again to Juanita. You will not insult her." His voice was very low and very quiet. "She is serving what the owner wishes, and you will thank Juanita and Miss Kent for their generosity. And if you say another word, I will slit your throat from ear to ear...."

Another man attempted to grab Eduardo, but one of the other miners caught his arm just in time to prevent the knife from sticking Blackie Hardesty.

Blackie glared murderously at Eduardo and then signaled his men to back off. They'd get the damned Mexicans later. Damned dark skins were always stealing the best of everything, from the best mines to the best women.

Juanita saw what was happening, and her hand was already on the gun that was always hidden underneath the rough counter. Slowly she released the gun's wooden stock as the men went back to drinking and Eduardo rejoined her behind the counter.

Juanita waited for Chalcie to call a halt to the largess, but she waited in vain. Chalcie downed first one glass of whiskey and then another, and Juanita could see from the flush that finally dispelled the pallor that Chalcie was going to feel very bad in the morning.

"That's it, men, we're all out. Come back tomorrow when we've had time to set up more bottles," Juanita finally said. The miners grumbled, fought and cursed as they tried to get out of the crowd. Eduardo moved in, helping the women close down the bar.

It was another hour before the C.K. was completely silent.

"Juanita, give me another one," Chalcie said, burping softly.

"I will not. What is wrong with you, drinking like that, and you, a girl who has never tasted the hard stuff in her life?'' Juanita grabbed Chalcie's shoulders and shook her. Chalcie's hair tumbled down around her face and neck, and she wobbled under Juanita's assault.

"Eduardo, I will speak to you later. Chalcie and I have some business, I believe," Juanita said.

Eduardo started to protest, then shrugged. As long as Juanita would come to him later he could be happy. It was the first time after all these months that she had even indicated that she noticed him. All in good time, he thought happily. All in good time.

"Well?"

"Well what?" Chalcie demanded angrily. "What did you expect from me? That I'd come back in and say that we made the business deal of the century? That Jordan would help me? That he would live up to what he offered me when I saved his damn place from burning down? Well he didn't, and there's no way I can win!"

Chalcie grabbed a tin can candle from the bar and marched toward the door, only wavering slightly as she aimed for the street.

Juanita watched in satisfaction, thinking it would do Chalcie some good to get into her room, strip off the fancy clothes and sleep off her disappointment.

Chalcie had other ideas, and Juanita watched in horror as she veered toward Jordan's Dry Gulch Saloon.

"Chalcie, no, come back here!" Juanita yelled, and ran after her boss, hiking up her skirts and leaping over the boxes that had been moved to the side of the building as she emptied all the liquor out of storage. She reached Chalcie just as she was about to burst through the door and confront Jordan on his own ground. Juanita grabbed Chalcie's arms and hauled her back, dumping her unceremoniously against the side wall.

"What do you think you're doing? He doesn't want to talk to you, and I can't say that I blame him." Juanita had tried very hard not to judge her friend, but it was becoming more difficult by the minute. Chalcie had thrown herself at

Jordan not out of lust or love but out of greed, and he had reacted the same way any normal man would. He had left her flat.

"You did this all yourself, Chalcie. You wouldn't listen to me. You had to have your way, didn't you?" Juanita accused as she herded Chalcie into her makeshift bedroom.

Chalcie stripped off the beautiful dress and drew on the hated pink calico. From the bed, Juanita heard the sobs begin and knew there was nothing she could do to help. Once Chalcie had sobered up, they could plan their next attack on whatever it was that was making Chalcie so unhappy.

Chalcie cried until there were no more tears left and the burning in her stomach had changed to a deep, painful ache. Even the whiskey couldn't blot out the despair she felt. Jordan had been just like her father when everything was said and done. He lied and he cheated and he took her for granted.

She fell heavily asleep while still plotting revenge.

The morning was no better. Chalcie had to deal with a terrible headache and the worst taste she had ever encountered in her mouth. It far outranked the bitter flavor of tansy that she had been subjected to in Mexico. If this was what whiskey did, she wasn't going to touch the stuff again.

"Even drunk, I struck one blow for myself, though," she consoled herself soddenly. That little binge of free drinks had probably cost her father a week's profits.

She didn't care. It wasn't her money. She was through worrying. And she had disrupted Jordan's profits at the same time. Not bad for half a night's work!

"The hell with you all," she snuffled as she stared into the early morning light. She knew she should have risen with the sun. There was work to be done, but she couldn't think of a reason to abide by her usual schedule. Who cared, anyway? Not her father, that was certain.

"Why should I work? There's nothing in it for me," Chalcie said belligerently. "I'd rather be off in the mountains, anyway, and that's where I'm going. A few days won't make any difference to anyone.''

She stood up, then sank slowly back to the bed as waves of the liquor-induced headache washed over her. She opened the chest and found the pants and shirt she had worn when she went to Jordan's house the night she met his cat. She was going to run away from home, that was what she was going to do. She laced up her heavy work boots. She tried to ignore the fine brown shoes that Mr. Tong had provided for her one night of romance and adventure. If that was romance and adventure, she decided, the rest of the world could have it, because she was going to live as a boring spinster for the rest of her life.

Chalcie grabbed her small container of salve for her burns, jammed her hat on her head and went out to the storage shed.

''So there you are, Chalcie. I don't know what's happened, but there isn't any bread for the miners, and the store isn't opened. Do you know…'' Juanita's voice slid to a halt as she looked at the ravaged features of her boss. Whiskey was bad for a woman; it made the flesh sag and the eyes red. But this was something far worse than plain whiskey. Chalcie looked as if everyone on earth had betrayed her.

''There isn't going to be any bread. Tell them all to go home,'' Chalcie said shortly. She didn't want to talk to Juanita. She didn't want to talk to anyone. She unfastened the lock and reached into the storage room to extract two tins of crackers, six tins of fine oysters and a large bag of jerky that had been bought from the Chinese earlier in the year. She could have managed in the mountains without the supplies, but at the moment, the idea of roughing it more than necessary wasn't very appealing.

''Chalcie, they depend on you for the bread,'' Juanita tried again.

''That's too bad. Give them baking lessons,'' Chalcie

said. She stuffed the supplies into a bag, shouldered the load and started down the street.

"But where are you going?"

"Up to the mountains."

"When will you be back?" Juanita couldn't believe this was happening. Chalcie, the one who was always working, was leaving everything?

"I'll be back when you see me. And in the meantime, cut the price of everything—drinks, food, women, gambling—by half," Chalcie said without looking back.

Juanita was so stunned she couldn't say a word.

Chalcie stopped, turned around and stared at her friend. "Did you hear me?"

"I did, but I can't believe that you mean it."

"Yes, Juanita, I want you to cut the price of everything by exactly half," Chalcie said again.

"But it'll drive you out of business. You've got to charge enough to cover the cost of supplies at least."

"Why?"

"Because you'll lose money and go out of business if you don't," Juanita maintained. She was beginning to feel as if she were talking to a changeling. Sometime in the night someone had sneaked into Chalcie's room and left a perfect replica of the woman that she knew, but the person doing the changing had neglected to copy the most important part of Chalcie—her brain and wit.

"We might go broke, mightn't we? When my father gets back, tell him to go ahead and send for the supplies. Let him and his precious Pete Ames take over. He can figure out how he's going to keep the places running, because I'm not going to do it," Chalcie said bitterly. "And if I come back and find that we've been driven out of business and taken Jordan de Chatain with us, then so much the better. With everything we have going for half price, he's going to have an interesting time trying to keep his place open and stocked with customers, isn't he?"

Chalcie turned back and headed off down the road, ignoring Juanita's pleas for her to come back.

Chalcie stayed up in the mountains for two weeks. She used every survival technique she'd learned from Estelle, one of the Indians in Sonora who had been willing to share her expertise with Chalcie once they became friends. She ate well and slept more than she had in years, and she sorted out her feelings about men, her life and her future. By the end of the two weeks, she had decided that men had no part in her life and that she was going to devote herself to building her own fortunes, rather than those of her father's. She was going to strike out on her own.

Chalcie finally decided it was time to return to Sonora. She walked to the edge of town and looked down the street. It was stifling, and after her time in the wilds, she was acutely aware of the smell of man and garbage. She had been gone only fourteen days, yet it felt like years.

She walked down the main street, nodding to the men as they passed by her. She had walked almost all the way down the street to the C. K. Saloon, when she heard a hated, dreaded, familiar voice from behind her.

"Chalcedony Kent, stop right there!" Jordan boomed at her. Several of the men on the street halted and looked around curiously, hoping they'd get a show that would break up the monotony of the camp life. Anything that happened between Chalcie and Jordan was bound to be like a free fireworks show.

Chalcie turned slowly and stiffened her back.

"Did you call me?" she asked coolly.

"You're damned right I did! Where have you been? I've been after Juanita every day to tell me what was going on. You cut the prices and run down your stock until there's nothing left. No one sees hide nor hair of you for days, and then, last night, I looked into your room, and your bed hasn't been slept in. What the hell is going on? I was worried...." Jordan shoved his hands in his pockets as if he'd

just become aware of what he'd said. He had been worried
about her, his worst competition, when he should have been
dancing in the street in celebration of the imminent demise
of the Kent bar and bakery.

"You looked in my room? You actually picked up the
curtain and looked into my own private room?" Chalcie
demanded furiously. How dare the man!

"I—" Jordan stepped back involuntarily as she raged at
him.

"Don't you give me any excuses. What the hell ever
gave you the idea you have any right to know where I've
been or what I've done? I'm not your property, I'm not
even your friend. Don't you ever think that you have any
rights whatsoever where I am concerned, do you understand
me?" Chalcie was yelling and she didn't care who heard
her.

"I'm sorry," Jordan said. It seemed as if he were always
apologizing to her, and all he'd wanted to do was make
certain she hadn't done something foolish like go out and
drown herself after he turned down her offer.

"What did you think I'd done, gone into a decline and
killed myself?" Chalcie challenged him.

The look on his face gave her the answer.

"You pompous, self-satisfied ass! You aren't worth dying over. You aren't even worth crying over! I went up to
the woods and had myself a nice comfortable rest, away
from everyone in this scurvy town including you and my
father. Now, get out of my way and let me get back to the
bar," Chalcie ordered him.

She tried to repress the small leap her heart had given
when she discovered he had been worried about her. He
was nothing to her and she was nothing except an irritant
to him.

"A woman alone, in the woods? You could have been
killed and no one would ever have found you!" Jordan was
astounded at the idea that Chalcie would go off on her own.
He'd heard James Kent come roaring back into town after

his fruitless search for the mother lode, demanding to see Chalcie and irritated because she wasn't immediately available. But Jordan hadn't realized that Chalcie had actually left town on her own.

"If you will excuse me?" She turned her back on him and began to walk away, satisfied that she had come to the right decision. She was going to leave all this behind her and strike out on her own.

"Chalcie…" Jordan called her, and she hesitated but didn't turn around. He was going to regret this. He knew he was, but he couldn't help saying it, just in case. "If you need anything, please ask me."

Chalcie's back stiffened even more, if that was possible, and she slowly turned toward Jordan de Chatain.

"What did you say?" she said, her tone so angry the sound of her voice vibrated in the street like the high-pitched whine of a rattlesnake.

Jordan shifted uncomfortably but stood his ground.

"I asked you to ask me if you need help."

"That's what I thought you said," Chalcie snarled. "I have humiliated myself once, Mr. de Chatain. I will never do so again. And as for your offer of help, it isn't worth the breath of air you've used to say it. Don't give empty promises and don't lie to me. Because one of these days, Mr. de Chatain, those promises that you've made and broken are going to come back and haunt you."

Chapter Seven

Almost seven weeks. Chalcie couldn't believe that it had been so long since she had returned from her pilgrimage to the hills. The distant mountains were rumbling with the thunder of approaching storms, and a cold wind swept down from the hills, bringing with it the scent of lightning and rain. All this time and her father still hadn't come to his senses. Pete Ames had done exactly what Chalcie had predicted. He'd already started to sell off everything they had accumulated. When she'd tried to talk to her father about it, he'd dismissed her without listening.

"He says the gold is going to peter out, and we'd better be ready to move on," had been her father's explanation, and there was nothing she could do to change his mind.

Chalcie was forced to watch helplessly as the whole empire that she had built was broken apart under Pete Ames's leadership. She walked slowly away from the building that had held the bakery, heading back to her room in the gathering darkness. The bakery had been sold and soon she knew that the boardinghouse would go and then something else, all of it part of a secret arrangement, with Pete Ames as the only beneficiary of the sales.

"Chalcie, could I see you for a moment?" Jordan stepped out from the deepening shadows as she walked back toward the bar.

Chalcie stopped dead in the street, her hand moving automatically to the knife she kept tucked into her waistband in a thin leather sheath.

"Whoa, nothing dangerous, I promise you," Jordan said as he saw the movement. He held up his hand to show that he wasn't threatening her.

Not a danger? Chalcie thought angrily. Of course he was a danger. He lied, he cheated and still he tried to make it seem as if he had done the only fair thing possible when he refused to sell her the land. And she was supposed to trust him when he popped out of nowhere in the dark?

"What do you want?" she asked suspiciously.

Jordan didn't answer immediately. Instead he fell into step beside her, walking with her for all the world as if he were her friend. She looked up at his dark handsome face and guileless eyes and wasn't the least bit impressed. It didn't matter how nicely he dressed or how fancy he tied his silk scarf or how sweet he talked to her, he wasn't her friend. He was as fake as the marked cards that he carried in the right front pocket of his vest to prove he could spot cheaters when no one else could. He proclaimed himself free of deceit, and then he cheated her out of land. In other words, she thought, he lied.

"You've closed the bakery?" Jordan asked conversationally. He needed something to break the ice, and the bakery was the most likely topic.

"I just sold all the flour we had to Will Seaton. He's starting his own bakery. I don't know if he's buying the bakery building, too, but I suppose someone is. Pete Ames thinks it would be a good idea," Chalcie said bitterly. She tried not to let anyone know how she felt about the way Pete Ames had come in and disrupted her life, but that wasn't easy to do when she felt sick to her stomach every time she thought about the man. Imagine, selling land instead of holding on to it! It was insane. Land was stability and permanence. Land was something to be retained at all costs.

"I'm not surprised that you've been driven to closing down the bakery. You've also stopped managing everything else for your father, haven't you?" Jordan asked. There was an edge to his voice that Chalcie hadn't heard before. "I know that things have changed in the past few months and your father is doing some strange things. As a matter of fact, it's your father I want to talk to you about."

"I don't talk about my father with strangers."

Jordan gritted his teeth in exasperation. He was going against all his instincts. He should have left her alone. He should have ignored all the things that he was hearing in the bar about her father. He should have simply refused to give in to an unreasoning desire to protect her. It was a foolish thing to do, because she was nothing to him. Yet for the first time in his life, he found himself responding as if he were actually in love with this woman. He wanted to make her life simple and pleasant. And to accomplish that, he had to talk to her about some unpleasant facts.

"Chalcie, your father is doing something that is completely irresponsible."

Jordan had finally realized what his part in this whole tragedy was. And since he had been the one to misjudge the situation, he had to at least try to reach her and warn her about the newest danger from her father's actions.

"Chalcie, please…"

"Why should I listen to you?"

"Because I feel responsible for what has happened to you over the last few weeks." Jordan had a hard time saying that. He hated feeling obligated to people, especially when it came to women. Yet he would have taken physical responsibility for her now, if she offered herself to him as she had before. But he had the awful feeling that she wouldn't ever give him a chance to reverse that first stupid decision on his part.

"Don't bother. It isn't your business."

"Damn it, yes it is," Jordan swore in front of her, he was so irritated.

Chalcie stared at him coldly.

He looked at her again and saw the sweet innocence behind all the toughness, and inwardly cursed himself and her father for making her life so hard. If only he'd listened when he had the chance, but no, he was too swollen with pride, too happy to be able to finally best Chalcie in the buying of the lot. He'd thought it was her fault that she didn't have enough cash on hand. He'd never realized the complications of handling the business when James Kent could step in and ruin everything. Just as Kent had set up the real ruination of Chalcie's life now.

"You wouldn't have come to me and offered yourself in exchange for land if you hadn't had a very good reason. There hasn't been too much love lost between us, and I should have understood that there was more behind your request than simple ownership of that damned piece of McClatchy's property."

Chalcie still didn't answer. Jordan shifted uncomfortably under her steady gaze. The blue eyes never wavered, the mobile, eminently kissable mouth didn't smile. Her face might have been carved from tanned marble as she listened to him.

Finally she sighed. "That no longer is your concern, since you have bought Brad McClatchy's land and have already started construction of another building." She stopped and looked at him critically, wondering just how deceitful he really was.

"However, it has occurred to me that it is unusual for a man like Will Seaton to have the money to buy a bakery, yet he does not seem to suffer from lack of funds." She was watching Jordan, looking for a sign that her guess was right. "It is possible, therefore, that you are continuing your depredations on the Kent land and have set him up to buy the bakery for you."

Jordan was shaking his head ruefully.

"I wish I was as sneaky as you seem to think I am. But no, Chalcie, I'm not buying the bakery through Will Seaton. My only concern now is what your father has cooked up for you.''

Chalcie started to turn and walk away. What was happening in her world was no business of his. For weeks she had been planning her escape from her father and Pete Ames. She was going to strike out on her own. She was saving the ten percent commission that she charged the men for storing their gold in her safe at the store. It wasn't much, but it would be enough to help her get started somewhere as a bar girl or a seamstress or a cook. There had been another gold strike up above Murphys, and it was far enough from Sonora that she might go over to the new digs and start her life again. A new name, new background, and Chalcedony Kent would disappear forever.

''I'm not going to let you walk away without telling you about what your father is doing.''

''So tell me,'' Chalcie said in exasperation. He could have said whatever he wanted and been done with it, instead of standing here in the middle of the street stammering like a schoolboy. ''You have one minute before I walk away. I don't like you, and I'm not interested in standing out here talking to you instead of getting on with some useful activity.'' She denied the excitement that his nearness caused. She wasn't going to have anything more to do with men, she reminded herself.

''Fair enough. Your father has written a new will. It's been drafted by Pete Ames, and he's showing it all over town and bragging about what he's done to whip you into shape as a real lady.'' Jordan's voice was scornful as he said the last words.

Chalcie could barely breathe.

What was he talking about? Her father would never do anything that would put her in jeopardy.

The thought crept in.

Pete Ames would do it and be happy to ruin her without ever giving her a chance to defend herself.

''What do you mean?'' Chalcie whispered.

"He's showing off a new will that has terms that are a disgrace."

"Why would it be a disgrace?"

Jordan didn't know how to tell her what her father had been saying. It was so private that he hadn't believed James Kent would talk about it in public, yet he had.

"Your father is convinced that the only way to turn you into a real gentlewoman is to find a way to marry you off. He's going to auction you off to the highest bidder. And if he dies before that happens, he's written a will…" Jordan didn't want to continue. He saw the expression on Chalcie's face and it tore him apart. He wanted to make the hurt go away, but he knew there wasn't a blessed thing he could do to shield her from her father's actions.

"What are the terms?"

Jordan ran a finger under his collar. This was harder than he had imagined it would be. He had thought that he would find her, tell her, then be on his way, his duty done and his conscience assuaged. He hadn't thought that she would look so terribly small and so devastated. He could see the pain in her face, and it hurt him. He didn't care that she was his enemy; no man had the right to give her this much agony.

He reached out to touch her arm, and she jerked away from him angrily.

"I don't need your pity, just your information. Tell me," she demanded.

"He has written the will so that you have only two choices when he dies. If you are not married already, you have one week to marry the man you love. If you are married by the end of that week, the Kent fortunes are given to your husband." Jordan hesitated again.

"Go on," Chalcie said. Her eyes were huge and underneath the tan she had gone white with the shock of his words. "What is the second choice?"

"You have one year to marry Pete Ames and he will then take control of your father's estate. If you do not marry, you are to gain nothing from your father's fortune. You will be left a pauper and half will go to Pete Ames, half to the miners' fund.''

Chalcie closed her eyes. She swayed for a moment and then sank to the ground, oblivious to the dust and red dirt. Her legs simply wouldn't hold her another instant. She heard a roaring in her head, and she leaned forward, her forehead against her knees.

"No," she whispered raggedly. "No, he can't do this to me."

Jordan knelt beside her. He didn't care that his black trousers were fast becoming black and red from the dust that was being ground into the cloth. He heard the pitiful whisper, and it tore at him. By some strange alchemy, he had come to feel responsible for her. He cared about her.

Jordan had stood there in the bar and heard the men plotting to woo Chalcie and get their hands on the fortune, and he knew that he had contributed to her trouble. If she had only had something of her own, she could have fought back. But Chalcie had no land and no funds in her own name, and her father knew the absolute power that he had over her life. It hadn't bothered James Kent one bit to hold his daughter up as a piece of meat to be bid on. If a man could win her heart, then he won the prize of money. And if no one won the prize, then Pete Ames took it all.

Jordan put his arms around Chalcie, and for once she didn't move away from his embrace. He reached under her chin to lift her face, and his hand was wet with tears.

"I'm sorry," Jordan said, his voice low. "I knew it would hurt you, but it would hurt more to have someone just blurt it out in front of a whole crowd, wouldn't it?"

Chalcie nodded reluctantly.

Jordan looked down at her woebegone expression. His heart went out to Chalcie. Slowly he leaned forward and cupped her face with his hands. He drew her close and kissed her. Her lips were just as soft as he had imagined they would be, and her exhalation of breath was sweet.

There was magic in the kiss, and promises he had never felt before.

Chalcie leaned forward, feeling the warmth of another human's hands on her, his lips on hers. It was a solace, a healing, something she had never experienced before. And then she felt the fire that began to grow as Jordan's lips lingered on her own. The warmth spread down her, touching her breasts and making her feel limp with cravings for more of his lovemaking.

Jordan put his arms around Chalcie and stood up, lifting her with him. He held her close and marveled at the lithe form that was hidden underneath the old pink dress that she wore. He kissed her cheek and tasted the saltiness of her tears, and then began to nuzzle her neck as he let her drift slowly downward until her feet reached the ground and his hands were on her breasts.

"No…" Chalcie moaned. "No, what are you doing?"

Jordan had kissed her. Jordan had actually put his hands on her body, and she had allowed it!

Jordan, her enemy, was trying to make love to her. She froze in his arms, and her mouth was no longer soft under his.

"Chalcie?" he asked dazedly, trying to recover his bearings. He'd been shaken by her sweetness more than he could admit.

"No, Mr. de Chatain, you will not win me and my father's lands with a kiss," Chalcie said furiously.

"What?"

"Stop playing the game. I'm not for sale to you or to anyone else. Don't you think I see what you're doing? Tell me the bad news and then be kind and considerate, and, before you know it, I'll marry you and you'll own everything in Sonora and I'll still have nothing. Well, it's not going to work."

Jordan let his arms drop, still dazed by the change in her. He had kissed her first out of sympathy, and then out of need, but the thought of seducing her for the Kent fortunes had never entered his mind.

"You little witch, I never would try and get your money through marriage. I don't care about the money...I just wanted to warn you, and I felt sorry for you," he lashed back at her.

"Don't bother. I can take care of myself," Chalcie said. But her body said another thing as he released her. She had never felt more alone in her life.

Jordan turned on his heel and began to walk away from her. He had gone nearly a hundred feet when he almost collided with Juanita.

"Jordan, have you seen Chalcie?" Juanita was out of breath and her usually neat hair was in complete disarray.

"She's back there," Jordan said, indicating the direction with a short movement of his head. He wasn't going to waste any energy on her. "What's wrong?" he asked.

"Something terrible—I think some of the fandango girls are dying," Juanita said. "We've got to get help and Doc Blake is so damn drunk he can't even see to look at a patient!"

"What's happening with the women?" Chalcie forced herself to respond to the urgency in Juanita's voice.

"They're throwing up, and Ellen and Rosie can't even move. Belly pains, cold and clammy, and they say that they can't see anything even when they open their eyes. I'm not certain that they can hear me when I talk to them. I don't know what to do!"

Chalcie didn't hesitate. She knew Johnny Tong was the only person who could help.

She was glad to have her heavy boots on as she traversed the trails that served the miners and the laborers who traveled to and from Chinese Camp each day. She was even happier when the moon sailed out from behind the clouds and lit her way with its pale light. At least it kept her from blundering into a sleepy rattlesnake lying on the warm rocks or into the path of someone who had had too much to drink.

Throwing up, stomach pains, can't see… All the symptoms sounded like the sickness that had stalked the crew and passengers on the ship bound for San Francisco. Chalcie and her father had managed to avoid the plague by buying food on shore when they stopped and never eating anything that was served to the other passengers.

She could hear the sounds of Chinese Camp ahead of her, the strange singsong tones of a different language. The scents were unfamiliar, slightly exotic, and she stopped for a moment, afraid to go into the area where, as far as she knew, no white woman had ever been before.

"I have to go," she said, then laughed aloud. Her father had her well trained. It had never occurred to her to tell Juanita to go and get Pete Ames and send him to Chinese Camp. No, she'd automatically taken over in the crisis. What would her father and Pete do when she took off for Murphys and they didn't have reliable little Chalcie to do the dirty work?

She stepped into the main area of the Camp, looking for something, anything, that would give her an idea where Johnny Tong might be found. There were huge vats of water steaming in front of one house and a series of smaller containers filled with delicious food in front of another hovel. The men looked at her and chattered, calling to one another as she walked by them.

"Johnny Tong?" she asked first one, and then the other, as she walked. "Please, Johnny Tong?"

None of them understood her. They shook their heads and smiled and looked down at the ground so they didn't have to meet her eyes. No one knew where he was to be found.

"Does anyone know where Johnny Tong is?" she called, hoping that by raising her voice she might get some response.

"Missy, you wanted to see me?" Suddenly Mr. Tong was beside her, leaning on his fancy cane. "You are not wearing the fine shoes?"

Chalcie looked down at her feet and shook her head.

"You want another pair?"

"No, I need your help—please, some of the women are very sick." Chalcie recounted the symptoms. "They need your help. I'm certain you have herbs and spices and such that can stop all this."

Mr. Tong nodded sagely. "Bad oysters. Others have had the same thing. I believe I can help. Let me gather a few things and we will go."

Mr. Tong left her on the street for a few moments and returned with a bag of herbs and spices. The delicate, gingery scent floated upward, melding with the other smells of the camp.

"Hurry," Chalcie said as she took off almost at a run. Mr. Tong plodded along behind her, his gait deceptively fast for a man encumbered with a cane and obviously arthritic.

As they made their way through town, they ignored the miners who passed and gawked at them. Even in a rough, lawless town such as Sonora it was considered improper for a white to be seen fraternizing with a Chinese. Chalcie couldn't think of anything but getting back to the bar and helping the women. She didn't notice when first one and then another miner ran ahead of them.

Chalcie hurried up the back stairs toward the second story of the bar, where the women worked. She reached the top stair and swung open the plank door, when she heard a muffled curse and the sound of a fist hitting human flesh.

"This'll teach you ever to come here. We don't like Chinese in our town."

Chalcie turned around and saw Mr. Tong being held at bay by two men. One man grabbed Mr. Tong, and the other began to beat the old man in the stomach.

"Stop it!" Chalcie screamed. She flew down the stairs. She had to stop them.

"Stop it, do you hear! I brought him to help the women!" She balled her hand into a fist and smashed the man holding Mr. Tong. He rocked with the blow and jumped backward, cursing.

Chalcie recognized the voice through the darkness. "Blackie Hardesty, what the hell are you doing here? You're supposed to be my friend," Chalcie gasped as she saw the man in the moonlight. She shook her hand to ease the pain of the blow.

"You bitch, don't you ever hit me again or I'll leave you as buzzard bait. No one, not even a woman, can do that! Now get out of here and leave us alone!" Hardesty snarled.

He tried to reach past Chalcie, and she swung at him again, connecting with his nose.

"Damn you, I'll kill you for that," he screamed. He swung at her. She came up low and inside and cracked his jaw with her fist. She heard his teeth clack together as she landed the blow.

"I said leave him alone!" Chalcie growled, her teeth clenched.

"Chalcie, get the hell out of here. I know what I'm doing."

Chalcie's head snapped up and she stared at the second man. Pete Ames? Why would he try to stop Mr. Tong from helping?

"What the hell are you doing here?"

"Just seeing to my own interests," Ames said smoothly.

"Well, your interests had better be the same as mine. And right now we need Mr. Tong. Call off Blackie Hardesty and get out of here. We need him for the girls. They're sick." Chalcie kept Blackie Hardesty at bay, dancing back and forth in front of him so he couldn't swing at her. She was glad that he was a lumbering man, slow in body as well as mind.

Pete Ames was another matter. She couldn't distract him the way she had Hardesty.

"Shut up, Chalcie. We don't need anything from any damned Chink," Pete said, and lunged toward Mr. Tong again. Somehow Mr. Tong wasn't in the same place that he had been a second before, and Pete stumbled and went to his knees. The old man brought his cane down over Ames's neck. The force of the blow shattered the cane, but it didn't stop Pete Ames.

"Now we'll see who is smarter, old man," Pete growled, and shook his head to clear it as he stood up. Then he lunged again, and this time his larger size and youth gave him the edge. Mr. Tong went down under the assault, his arthritic knees making it impossible for him to move out of Ames's way fast enough.

"Damn you, you idiot!" Chalcie screamed at Ames. Where was her father when she needed him? He should be there, watching how his wonderful partner looked out for their interests. Instead, Ames was keeping the only man who could help the girls away from them. She was distracted for just a moment and Blackie Hardesty came toward her, slamming her to the wall. She felt his bulk against her, his body hot and stinking as he forced her to give in to his superior weight. She was effectively taken out of the fight.

In one awful second, she knew then that Mr. Tong was going to be murdered.

Suddenly Pete Ames was sprawled in the dust, his eyes closed and blood trickling from his mouth. Blackie Hardesty squawked as he was swung around and punched twice, once in the belly and then an upper cut on the chin, the second of the night. He collapsed, out cold, on top of his boss. One man stood above them, wiping his hand on his pants. Jordan de Chatain stepped over the bodies.

"Did he hurt you?" Jordan gathered Chalcie in his arms, his face white in the moonlight. "I heard something and stepped out back and saw these men..." He gestured toward the two, who were just beginning to move against the assault. "Luckily, Ben was right behind me or I might not have been able to save you."

"Thank you," Chalcie said. "Mr. Tong?" She looked around, afraid that she would see him beside the other men, crumpled in an unconscious heap.

"Everything is fine. Thank you, Mr. de Chatain, for the help." Mr. Tong leaned down and gathered the remnants of his stick and shook his head. "This old friend has been with me a long time. At least he died in an honorable battle."

He picked up the bag of herbs he had been carrying from his shop. "May I go up and see your women?" He was composed, cool, as if nothing had ever happened.

"Upstairs," Chalcie croaked. She knew that Juanita didn't approve of drinking, but she definitely deserved one after tonight. She was past shaking.

Jordan let Chalcie move away from him.

She looked at him, her face cold and indifferent. "I guess we're even now. I've saved you from a fire, and you've saved me from something even worse. Let's call it even and stay out of each other's way, all right?"

"I'm not going to make any promises, Chalcie," Jordan said, letting his hands drop. The feel of her body was imprinted on him, the taste of her lips was still sweet on his mouth. No, he'd make no promises.

Chapter Eight

Chalcie fought against the nightmare, crying out as she tried to force her father to give in. "You can't do this to me...I'm the reason you have money," she was saying, trying to make her father focus on her instead of fading in and out of the shadows.

"It was me, don't you understand? It was my idea to make money...." She had to win. She had to tell him he was wrong to treat her like this. Her hand struck out, hitting something soft. "The women, the women will die and we won't have anything left!"

"Ouch, damn it, hold her hands," someone whispered. "She clips me on the chin again and I'm going to rattle her brain a good one. Damn it, her fists really pack a wallop."

"We've got to get her away from here under her own power. Sure as hell, someone will see her if we try and take her out slung over my shoulders."

There were other mutters and the hiss of a rope as it was unslung from a belt. They were ready for her.

Chalcie shook her head. Her mind tried to play with the sounds, to make them less real. She was so tired, all she wanted to do was sleep, but the voices called her back to consciousness.

"Make certain she doesn't get away. I don't want any

racing around in the dark. There's too much at stake,'' Ames said.

"She's not going anywhere."

"Okay, wake her up."

Ames shook her shoulder. "Chalcie, your father needs you."

A male voice, rough and slurred, dragged her from her nightmare of trying to convince her father that she was his rightful heir.

She moaned. She wanted to sleep, not to wake up. Her body cried out for rest. She didn't want to have another crisis.

"Damn you, woman, get up now!"

Hands shook her shoulders, whipping her head back and forth as a second voice chimed in.

Chalcie was dragged back to consciousness. "What's wrong, what time is it?" She could barely talk. There was no light in the room. Far away she could hear the screams and gunshots that punctuated the night.

"Your father's been shot. We're supposed to take you down to Doc Blake's."

Chalcie shook her head and tried to close her eyes again. This was just a continuation of the nightmare. There hadn't been any shooting, and her father was fine. She was probably dreaming it because she was so angry at him for tearing apart her lovingly created empire. She'd have to tell him about the dream. He'd laugh at it, once he got over being offended that she could dare dream him dead.

"Come on, Chalcie."

She knew that voice, and it had no place in her dreams. What was Pete Ames doing in her room?

"I think your father is dead."

Gradually the words began to sink in, and she awoke enough to wonder why a nightmare had the feeling of reality to it. She rubbed at her eyes.

"You're lying. My father can't be dead. He's down hav-

ing a drink." Chalcie shook her head, trying to make sense
of what she was hearing.

Her father couldn't be dead. She hadn't had a chance to
talk to him about his will. Even her father couldn't be that
unfair! He wouldn't dare leave her to fight it out with Pete
Ames for control of the fortune.

Reality, however, pushed her relentlessly into consciousness. These people weren't joking and this was real life,
not a nightmare.

"No, it's not possible." She sat up and brushed the
hands away from her. "Why would he be dead?"

"A fight with someone," Ames told her. "We don't
know who. All we heard were the shots. When we ran out
of the bar, there he was lying out in the dusty street like
he was asleep, but there was a bullet hole clean through
his forehead." Ames obviously enjoyed telling the story to
Chalcie.

With shaking hands she moved to the lamp and lighted
it. The darkness crept back to the corners, and she could
see that the two men with her were Pete Ames and her
father's no-good hired hand, Houlihan.

For a moment she dismissed the news that they brought
her. Of course they were wrong. Her father would come
tramping in during the early morning hours and they would
have a good laugh about Ames and Houlihan trying to play
a joke on her.

Then she realized—Houlihan! He had returned from
Stockton, and ahead of the storm, even if only by a few
hours.

"Houlihan, what the hell are you doing here? When did
you get back?" She focused desperately on the men, trying
to blot out what they had been saying about her father. It
was a miracle; the man her father had sent down to buy
supplies in Stockton was finally back, hopefully with all
the supplies they'd need to get through the winter.

Ames scowled at her. "When he came into town doesn't

matter. We were sent to bring you back to Doc Blake's. It's a good thing you're still dressed.''

She looked down at herself and was mildly surprised to find that she had gone to bed without removing her dress. She knew she couldn't postpone facing reality any longer. Without looking to see if they were following her, she opened the calico curtain and started down the road toward Doc Blake's.

She was numb. Her father was dead? Then that brought the will into force, and she didn't even really know what the legal document said. The will—if her father had bragged all over town about writing and signing the will, then everyone would know about it. Not a chance in the world of simply ignoring it, canceling all the sales and stepping back into managing the businesses and carrying on as usual.

What was she going to do? She couldn't marry Ames. The man was slimy, a liar and a cheat who would run everything into the ground in a matter of months.

What was it Jordan had said? She had one week to find someone else to marry her? A sneaking thought about Jordan de Chatain crept into her head and she promptly dismissed it. He wasn't even a possibility. Still, she was angry enough with her father, even dead, that she thought about the revenge of marrying his worst enemy.

She'd go to Doc Blake's, make arrangements for the body to be taken care of, she thought numbly, and then she'd have to think about what her life would be like without her father. She had walked several yards beyond the light when she heard a rushing sound behind her. Turning, she saw only a black shape.

Ames reached out and grabbed her, whirling her around.

''Get her now!'' he ordered urgently. His hands bit into her arms.

''What…?'' She started to cry, but was cut off as a blow came crashing down on her head. It took only a moment to truss her with the sack over her head and a cord around her hands. She was caught and thrown over the back of a horse and lashed in place. Chalcie moaned and was enveloped in a blackness that threatened to suffocate her. There was no air.... The world faded to darkness. She didn't even feel the movement of the horse as they started the long trek up the mountainside.

"See, what did I tell you? Nothing to it. She stays out of circulation for a week and she'll have to marry me. So I'll still get everything Kent ever had. Stupid old man, giving his wealth to a stranger instead of his own family," Ames said in satisfaction. His delighted grin couldn't be seen in the dark, but his words were framed with gloating satisfaction.

Ames rode another horse, and Houlihan followed with a mule laden with a week's worth of supplies.

Neither Houlihan nor Ames noticed the Indian woman who watched the procession head out of Sonora and north toward the summer mining camps. Estelle kept mostly to herself. The only white people she had ever talked to were Chalcie and Jordan, and that was only because both of them had taken the time to learn a rudimentary form of Miwok so they could communicate with the Indians in the area. Estelle saw clearly that Chalcie was being abducted, but she didn't know what to do about it. Who could she tell? And what if she was wrong? What if this was one of the more bizarre white man's customs?

Estelle faded into the background again, fingering the thick wool blanket that she used as protection against the biting wind. She should do something, but what?

Chalcedony was oblivious to everything. The jolting of the horse did not awaken her as they bumped up the trail toward the mountains. The lashings of rawhide and hemp cut into her wrists, but she didn't respond to the pain.

Ames kept an eye on the hostage, and as the miles upward were covered without any sign of life from Chalcedony, he scowled, worried, and finally called a halt to remove the sack from her head and check that she still had a pulse.

"Damn you, Houlihan, you didn't have to hit her so hard. I want her to live to enjoy being married to me," Ames said, and for the first time an evil grin slashed across his handsome face.

"Didn't hit her that hard. She's just playing," Houlihan said sourly.

Ames ignored the man. Houlihan would be dead before the end of the week, if he had anything to say about it.

Chalcedony finally awakened as Ames was taking her off the horse. She felt as if every inch of her body had been beaten. Her head ached, her stomach hurt, and her legs were too rubbery even to make the attempt to stand. She couldn't think, either. The blow to the head had made everything seem fuzzy and disconnected. She could remember something about her father and a warning from Jordan, but nothing else.

Chalcie moaned and struggled feebly against the restraints. She fought to make her eyes open and finally focused on the rough cabin in front of her. It looked like a summer camp that someone had abandoned. The plank door was secured against the depredations of the bears and raccoons in the area, and one hole had been cut in the side wall to serve as a window when it was unboarded.

Ames pulled out a wicked-looking knife and cut through the leather thongs that held the door closed. He didn't want to waste time untying the knots.

"Throw her in there on the bed," he instructed Houlihan. "She's not likely to fight too much with that knot on her head." Houlihan complied, tossing her down on the filthy wooden cot that stood in the corner.

Chalcedony coughed as the dust rose from the mildewed and moth-eaten bear pelt. She gagged and almost retched at the smell from the cabin. She tried to sit up, but the pain in her head blinded her, making her see stars and then nothing.

* * *

Chalcie drifted in and out of consciousness for several days. Her dreams were violent, someone forcing a scalding liquid down her throat, then liquor. She had fought against the ministration, wanting to avoid the pain.

Finally she could retreat no more.

Pete Ames caught the movement in the bed and stood up. "So, you're back with us. For a while we thought we'd lost you. Bad luck if we had. The miners tend to be touchy about murdering a lady. I'm real glad, honey, to see that you have survival potential." Ames's voice was chillingly calm. "If you died right away, so soon after your father, someone might begin to wonder what happened to the Kent family. We'd hate to have them asking questions, Houlihan and I would."

"Murder," Chalcie said faintly. Suddenly everything fell into place. She remembered what had happened. Pete Ames had killed her father and kidnapped her, all with the intent of taking every cent of the Kent fortune for himself.

The bastard! she thought. The unmitigated gold-plated son-of-a-bitch; he would not get away with this. Silently she vowed that he would pay for both crimes. With any luck, he would be hanging from a tree in Sonora before the month was out. She knew the miners. They'd put up with Ames and Houlihan killing someone—that happened occasionally. But the miners would not be tolerant of someone who sought to bedevil one of the few honest and upright women in the gold camp.

Ames would hang for kidnapping her, if not for her father's death. She would make certain of that. But to avenge the murder, she had to survive. No one else would ever care enough to ask questions about what must look like a random shooting.

Damn the man anyway. She wouldn't even be there to see her father buried. It was clear that Ames intended to keep her up in the mountains for the full week. He didn't want her to find anyone else to marry. Did she honestly think she would rather marry him than go without a penny of the

Kent money? If he believed that, he had no idea how repulsive he was to her.

How had he done it? she wondered hazily. She knew most of the gossip around town, and word had it that Ames was a good shot, for a lawyer. How had Ames managed to kill her father? Her father was one of the most cautious men alive. He was overbearing, loud and prone to rash decisions, but he always covered his back and was careful around men with guns. Perhaps it had been up close, where a small pistol could have done the damage.... Or had Ames been waiting, out of sight, lurking with a rifle at his shoulder, ready for the time her father stumbled out of some bar?

She would never know.

She faded out of consciousness again.

It was another full day before the pain and disorientation from the crack on her head finally diminished and she was able to plan.

First, she thought, she had to escape; second, she had to marry someone else; and third, she had to see Ames punished. Already she was thinking of various ways she could make a getaway from the cabin and leave both Ames and Houlihan incapacitated.

Ames and Houlihan were still asleep when she opened her eyes again and looked around her. She had been dreaming of escaping and she had been convinced that once she saw the clearing in the daylight, she would be able to see the path that would lead her back to Sonora.

The mountains, however, were subtly different. The cabin was high, far beyond the last scraggly trees, and the air was crisp and cold, foreshadowing the snow that could fall at any time. There was no smoke in the air. That meant they were at someone's summer shack, far away from other miners and claim jumpers. Even a hint of smoke would have given her hope—it would have meant another miner nearby who could help her. She wished unreasonably that Jordan was close. He'd help her get out of this mess. He would have cared.

Chalcie was still scanning the horizon for some familiar landmark that would lead her back to Sonora, when she felt Ames's hand on her back in an intimate touch.

"We'll be staying here for a while, darling, just enough time to get acquainted."

He moved his hand in a lazy circle, caressing her skin underneath the bodice, despite Chalcie flinching away from him. The message was clear. She was in his hands. He could do anything he wanted with her.

Jordan—it hadn't felt that way with Jordan. When he'd touched her, there was warmth and gentleness. She had leaned into him, feeling his body, and she had wanted his kisses and caresses to last. The sensation was nothing at all like the one Pete caused. When Pete touched her, she wanted to throw up.

She moved away from him. She would outsmart him. Ames would make a mistake sometime, and then she'd be given a chance to run away.

"Get up and fix us a meal, and then you can do something about this cabin. I'm going out to see if there are any rabbits around for meat," Ames said when Chalcie was finally able to walk under her own power again.

"I'm not your slave, and I will not cook and clean for you. Do your own dirty work," Chalcie told him.

Ames walked over to her, slapped her hard on the side of the face and grabbed her by the hair when she started to fall from the force of the blow.

Chalcie fought to keep from crying. She wasn't going to give him the satisfaction of knowing that he'd hurt her.

"Now, let's try that again. I'd hate like hell to have you unconscious on that bed for another couple of days, but if that's the way you want it, that's the way it'll be." Ames's voice was quiet and smooth and filled with menace. "I can keep you here past the seven days, remember. You've already been here five days."

Chalcie was stubborn, but she wasn't stupid. She needed to be able to escape, and if Ames kept hitting her, she'd never have enough of her wits about her to come up with a way to disable the men and leave the cabin.

Sullenly she nodded and Ames laughed in satisfaction. He had won. "Next time you'll know to do whatever I want."

After she washed herself as best she could, Chalcie set about cleaning the cabin, and as she did, she concentrated on planning her escape. She knew that she was running close to the edge of the week that her father had given her to marry someone else. She would have to escape that afternoon or risk missing the deadline.

She heard only one shot in the hills that afternoon and contented herself with thinking that Ames had seen game once and had missed. She had heard all about his reputation as a fairly good shot and she didn't believe it. Of course, part of her reluctance to believe his marksmanship rested on her half-formed plans to try to run away from him. She wasn't partial to the thought of receiving a blast in the middle of her back when she was a mile downhill and almost safely away from the bastard.

"Here's a rabbit. Do something with it." Ames came back later that afternoon and threw the bloody carcass at her.

Chalcie's lips tightened as she looked at the poor thing. So he was a good marksman. Well, she'd just have to find a way to make it so that he couldn't shoot at her, then, wouldn't she? She skinned the animal and used the last of the onions and several potatoes to begin the stew. There would be almost nothing to cook for another meal the next day.

A glimmer of an idea came to her. It wasn't the first time that she'd had to rely on the land for her food; even during her two weeks in the mountains, she had foraged for some of her grub. She would wager that she knew more about the wild plants around the mountains than these men ever would. And that might give her the chance to escape that she needed. She had noticed something down below the camp, at the tree line. It was something that the men would have ignored, but it might be her key to freedom.

She could see Ames watching her, and she was vividly conscious of every movement that would remind him she was a woman. He had made no move toward her yet, other than a few caresses, but she knew she wouldn't be able to count on that kind of restraint for too much longer. His eyes following the curve of her breasts and thighs told her that.

He shook his head in reproof. "Stop glaring at me. You don't have to like me, just as long as we do finally marry and I get to keep every little gold flake of the Kent fortunes. With your help, of course."

Chalcie stared at him, her gaze level. How many other men and women had been taken in by that sweet exterior, the wide smile and the guileless blue eyes? Underneath it all was something as desperate and dangerous as a rattlesnake. He didn't know it, but he was dead. She'd dealt with snakes before.

"You just don't want me to walk away from it all, because if I don't marry you, you'll never be able to collect everything. If I leave, only half of it comes to you and the other half goes to the miners. You'd never give up that much money willingly, would you?" Chalcie's tone was jeering.

"Glad to see you understand my reasoning. So don't try anything rash, and we'll both come out of this adventure ahead of the game," Ames said, his voice soft. "Remember, I can always bend you to my wishes." He smiled. "It wouldn't be the first time a woman was forced to accept a man."

Chalcie shuddered. "I have to go down there and gather some greens for the stew," she said, almost tripping in her haste to get away from him.

He didn't seem to be watching her too closely as she began to make her way down the hillside toward the herbs that she wanted to gather for supper, but there was always an air of tenseness around him, so she couldn't be certain. From the looks of him, he seemed to be casually picking his fingernails with a wicked-looking knife. But looks could be deceiving. She wished she could remember if there had been any stories about his prowess with a knife.... Did she dare make a break for it?

She bent down to pick some of the plants that looked like wild onions and miner's lettuce. She rubbed the leaves on the tall green plant and smiled. There was no onion scent about them, and that was exactly what she wanted. Gently she extracted the innocent-looking white globes from the earth. Now she needed several other herbs to make the stew more palatable.

"I've got to go down a little farther. There's something down there we can eat," Chalcie called back to Ames.

She wished she had on her pants and heavy boots as she tried to maneuver down the hillside. The red mud and rocks were slick with the rains that had been falling for the past few weeks. Chalcie knew that if she took an accidental tumble, she might end up with a knife sticking out of her back just because Ames was nervous. She breathed a sigh of relief as she reached the first of the trees. Even stunted, the gnarled tree was taller than she was and had a cushiony softness around the base where the needles had fallen for hundreds of years. She bent down to loosen the dry white-and-brown caps that grew around the base of the thin, stunted trunk, exulting as she looked at them. She didn't have any way to test the mushrooms as Estelle had taught her, but she was almost certain she knew what they were. She stood up and wavered to one side. She was weak and still nauseated from the blow to the head. But she had to keep on. If she failed now, she might be tied to this lunatic for the rest of her life.

"That's enough, darling," Ames said, straightening lazily. He hefted the knife by the blade, delicately balancing it, ready to throw. "I don't think you'd like this sticking out of your back just because you happened to go a little too far into the undergrowth. I'd hate to panic and think I couldn't catch my little gold mine.''

Ames's boyish face was alight with amusement. He thought it was all a grand joke. He'd always wanted to be rich without working for it. This was his chance and nothing, not even Chalcie, was going to stop him. The very fact that he would bring her down from the mountain, safe and secure, would satisfy everyone of his good intentions. They would all understand that he had simply taken steps to assure that he received what was actually his under the terms of the will. Not only was everything fair in love and war, he thought, it was also fair in greed.

Chalcie looked at him as she would a slug in the middle of her garden.

''Did my father know about you? How did you manage to make him ignore this side of you?'' Chalcie climbed back up the hill and confronted the man. She was genuinely puzzled. Her father had never been known for being a wonderful judge of character, but Ames was too slimy for even her father to have been taken in for long.

''Why, darling, as you'll soon find out, I'm a charming young man, serious and truly interested in everything about you. I tricked your father, no reason I can't trick you.''

He flicked the blade between them, a silent warning. ''Besides, he wanted you to be safe, and I promised to give him his heart's wish. It's so easy to take advantage of people!''

He laughed again, and the sound pealed out through the clear mountain air.

Chalcie ignored him, though her hands were white around the potherbs she had gathered.

''Maybe I should introduce you to the delights of married life. I'm sure that Houlihan wouldn't mind sleeping outside. And I do need some relaxation. Guarding you is so tedious.''

Ames laughed as she moved away from him.

He was talking about bedding her? She'd rather die. She

looked up as the first snowflakes of the first storm of winter began to fall. She'd rather freeze to death on a mad dash down the hill than stay around and let Ames have his way with her. She had never been a woman to just sit back and let things happen to her. She wasn't about to fold under the pressure and let Ames do whatever he wanted now!

"All right, if you don't like the idea of being introduced to lovemaking, then get busy and put something edible together," Ames growled.

Chalcie smiled. So her plan was going to have a chance after all.

Slowly she went over to the fire and added more fuel. She cut up the new herbs and added them to the already simmering stew. They may think they had won this round, but they didn't know that Chalcie Kent didn't give up.

She kept her back to the men, hoping they would interpret this as a sign of her submission. What she really wanted to do was to make certain they didn't see what she was up to.

She mixed biscuits from the last of the flour, saving just a bit to thicken the stew. It was already beginning to smell good. She slid the pan of saleratus biscuits to the edge of the fire to cook, watching carefully as they began to rise. The smell of the bread almost covered Houlihan's stink.

"At least she can cook," she heard Houlihan say sotto voce to Ames. He was answered by an inarticulate snarl.

Chalcie shivered. If she ever had to face Ames again, she knew that he'd do everything in his power to make her pay for what she was planning to do to him. She knew he had not been joking when he said he would murder her, and she had no illusions about his intelligence. He was smart enough to make murder look like an accident.

Please, please, let me be right… she prayed silently. She was almost certain she had chosen the right plants; but if she had guessed wrong, her life was going to be short, ugly and come to a fast and brutal end. She broke a few more pieces of the mushroom into the stew. It was better to overdose than to have the men recover and take vengeance on her.

Chalcie shivered at the thought. Humiliation, beatings, years of living with a man who would hurt her daily—that would be the retribution Ames would give her. She couldn't stand living like that. She had to do this right the first time.

No matter what else happened, no matter what risks she took, she had to make a break for it. Maybe her father had been lucky. At least he'd only had to suffer for a moment before he died. He had set the stage for years of suffering if she gave in and married Ames. She knew she should have been mourning her father, but she was still too angry. How dare he put her in such a position—marry or start with nothing to her name but the clothes that she wore? He must have hated her to have done this to her.

She looked at the boiling stew and hoped that she had gathered enough of everything. She didn't have much to go on, only what Estelle had taught her and the tales brought in by other miners about men who had almost starved to death, then had died from having eaten the wrong thing. This was her one chance to escape. If she missed, Ames and Houlihan would be on their guard.

Swiftly she gathered the plates and bowls that needed to be scrubbed clean in preparation for the next meal. Those dishes, the herbs and the black iron pot would be her salvation. Excitement began to bubble as she realized that her plan just might work.

"Where the hell do you think you're going?" Ames demanded as she took the dishes out to the small stream that ran down the mountain. She noticed that he had his knife out and he looked just a little bit twitchy-fingered with the blade as he talked to her.

"I'm going to clean this mess up, then I'll start serving the stew," Chalcie challenged him. She wasn't going to let him know with even a trace of a flinch that he frightened her almost beyond reason.

"Stay where I can watch you. Looks like you'll turn out to be a good wife after all, for as long as you last."

One hour later she set the bowls of stew before Houlihan and Ames.

"Eat it in good health," Chalcie said, and smiled at them sweetly.

"Your temper won't win you anything, Chalcie. Never mind, just another day and I'll have a chance to beat it out of you."

"Aren't you eating?" Houlihan noticed that she hadn't served herself yet. He had the vague feeling that he shouldn't trust her, but the rich smell of the stew dulled his worries. The thick slices of onion and other herbs made his mouth water.

Chalcie smiled as she looked down at the sparse dinner she had served herself. They would never know what killed them. She knew she'd have to eat something, but she could only hope that it would be just enough to make her sick, not to kill her.

"I'm eating. I'm not going to let you win because I starved myself to death," Chalcie said as she sat opposite them.

She took three biscuits from the stained black pan and added them to the spoonful of stew she had taken. She didn't dare sit down with nothing at all on her plate.

"That's not enough," Ames said flatly.

"It's enough for me. You've bashed me on the head, you've kept me leashed like a dog and threatened me…do you expect me to eat like a trencherman?" Chalcie asked.

Ames looked at her shrewdly but finally subsided. Overcome with hunger and the promise of a nourishing meal, he began to eat his stew. Chalcie didn't dare let her eyes stay on the food; it might warn him of what was going to happen. But every bite registered with her.

They never noticed that all she ate were the biscuits. She couldn't avoid the stew completely, the biscuits had been soaked in the gravy, but she tried her best not to eat more than a spoonful of the deadly brew.

Ames didn't taste anything wrong. He consumed the whole bowl and ordered her to get him more.

Chalcie served him silently but with an inner feeling of elation. It was going to work!

Chalcie cleared away the dishes as the men relaxed. Then she waited, leaning back against the bed and watching as they both began to fall asleep.

Within an hour Ames was trying desperately to focus his eyes. He looked around the room and saw that both Chalcie and Houlihan were sound asleep.

"Damn you, I've never been so tired in my life. Can't seem to keep my eyes open."

He knew something was amiss but didn't know what. Chalcie heard him and tried desperately to keep from smiling in triumph. She kept her eyes closed and her face calm.

He reached out for something to use to pull himself up, and the chair that he grabbed creaked and splintered under his weight. He almost fell on Chalcie as he tried to shake her to wake her up.

"Help me, you bitch, I'm sick...." He leaned heavily against the rough wooden walls.

Chalcie pretended to wake from a deep sleep. She stretched and yawned.

"What's wrong?" she asked curiously. Inwardly she was exultant. It was working!

"Sick, stomach hurts, and I see two of everything. I thought you poisoned us...but you ate, too. It has to be cholera...." Ames looked up at her. His eyes were feverish and his face red. His blond hair was matted with perspiration and his brilliant blue eyes were dulled. He was a thoroughly ill man.

"Cholera...I can't do anything about that," Chalcie said, and moved away from him.

"You have to take me to Sonora. I'll die without help." Ames was pleading now. He fell to the floor, his face pressed against the blessedly cool dirt. The sweat poured down his face. He tried to raise a hand to wipe it away, but he didn't have the strength.

"Water, please." His voice was a croak of despair. Suddenly he looked his age, every bit of the thirty-five years that had been given over to debauchery, lechery and thievery.

"I'll bring you water, but I can't take you to Sonora."

She gave him a drink of water and then backed away as he spilled it on the floor. She couldn't risk having him catch her now.

"The horse, the horse will take you to Sonora for help..." Ames pleaded. Within a few moments he was totally unconscious.

Chalcie felt for his pulse. It was racing and thready. She began to edge toward the door.

Ames opened his eyes one last time as he started to cough. His face began to turn blue as he fought for breath.

He fell back against the hard pallet, panting, looking at her with the confusion of a man who has lost touch with reality. His eyes closed softly. There was one long last sigh.

Houlihan had never regained consciousness, and now Ames was gone. She didn't wait to check his pulse. She simply ran out of the cabin and toward the paddock where the horses were kept. She could ride Ames's mare, she was sure. There wasn't time even to slip a bridle over the horse's head. At any moment she expected to be caught in the back with a blast from a gun.

"This is it, horse, our only chance," Chalcie said as she used one of the logs of the fence to boost herself into position on the mare's back.

It was already dark and she knew she had less than twenty-four hours to find a man or lose everything.

Chapter Nine

Chalcie grabbed the horse's mane. She was glad for the months that she had ridden bareback down in Texas. She was at home with the rough bristle of the horse's hide against her legs.

"Come on, pretty girl, let's get away from those bastards," she said as she urged the mare to a trot. She ducked as the first low branches of the scrub pine swept over them. All she wanted was to put as many miles between herself and the cabin as possible. She hadn't really expected that the dried-out browned mushrooms would do their job.

She had done it. She had managed to outwit both Ames and Houlihan. It had been her brains and cunning against their brawn and she had managed to defeat them. The thought gave her a warm feeling. She could take care of herself, she was certain. She could walk away from Sonora and everything that was there and still be able to survive.

She may not have to walk away from everything… Chalcie thought suddenly. If her father had meant to give all the holdings to Pete Ames and he was dead, then she still might have control of the land, buildings and mines. Unless, of course, the miners' fund challenged her and took everything itself, leaving her with nothing.

She could still outwit the will by getting back before the week was over and marrying someone. Who could she find who would promise to give her back the Kent fortunes after they married? Chalcie racked her brains as she rode downward. There was not one man among the thousand in Sonora that she could trust to live up to an agreement made before marriage.

"I'll think of something," Chalcie promised herself, but at the moment, the terror of the day, coupled with the taste of stew that she had eaten, was making her dizzy and so tired that she would gladly have fallen off the horse and slept for a year underneath the limbs of the evergreens.

She didn't even know which way they should be heading. She had jumped on the horse and headed downward, not really caring about anything except leaving Ames and Houlihan behind. She knew she could survive if she got lost. She could build herself a shelter and find something to eat, but she would rather make it to Sonora and find a husband before her father's will had a chance to come into effect.

What was it Ames had said…give the mare her head and she would find her way home? Chalcedony leaned forward and knotted the long strands of mane in her hand. She hoped the mare knew the direction. She didn't even have a hint about where Sonora was. She would have felt a lot better about heading down the hill if she'd been able to see some smoke on the horizon or some other sign of civilization. She knew all too well that more than one poor soul had starved to death or died of exposure up in the hills when they became disoriented or just plain lost.

"Come on, honey, the faster we get there, the faster we'll both be able to rest."

Oh God, she was so tired. Every bone in her body ached, every muscle screamed in protest. If there had been a way to hole up until morning she would have done it. But there was no time. It was getting colder and colder on the mountain, and the storms that had swept over the hills and then retreated began to swirl down again on the dark mountainsides.

And Jordan—what would Jordan think of what had happened to her?

"No!" Chalcie said, startling the mare with the sound of her voice. "No, I'm not going to talk to Jordan. There's no reason to. He wouldn't care whether I disappeared off the face of the earth. In fact, he'd probably be glad to have me gone." Chalcie leaned closer to the mare's ears to confide, "But did you know, he has the nicest eyes, and I thought he was very gentle with me when he cleaned up all the blood. Oh, mare, I bled all over him, and he didn't even yell when he saw what I did to his shirt!"

Of course he had made up for not yelling about the shirt by the way he had carried on when she put out the fire.

"His kiss was sweet. I wished it could have lasted longer," Chalcie said. The mare twitched her ears. "I don't suppose that it meant anything to him. I know it didn't mean anything to me."

It didn't make sense. Jordan was still her enemy. Men in general seemed to be taking great care to see that she was unable to look on them as friends. Even her own father had ultimately been her enemy, too.

Her father. Now he was dead and she'd never have a chance to resolve all the differences they'd had.

"We had our fights, and I thought he was a fool for taking in Ames, but, oh God, I would have done anything possible to get him out of the man's clutches if I had thought it would end this way. My father dead, murdered, and all by a partner!"

Strange that her father had always had these troubles, and in the end, his quest for the perfect partner had killed him and taken away her chance to have both wealth and a normal life.

Chalcie's heart ached, though, to think that her father could have treated her in such a callous manner. Had he never even thought of her feelings when such a will was read in public? For someone who wanted her to be treated like a fine lady, he had done everything he could to make certain that she was so shamed that she could never show her face in polite society again.

And now Ames... Even the thought of him made her sick. She felt light-headed and slightly unreal. Even the tiny bit of the mushroom stew that she had eaten was affecting her equilibrium.

She twined her hand more thoroughly in the horse's mane and urged the mare on with gentle words and occasional pats to her neck. Surprisingly, they worked well together. There was a curious tensing in the animal's muscles when she came to an obstruction. Chalcie soon learned to read the mare's movements and to duck and hide her face against the horse's mane to escape the worst of the brush and the tree branches. Flattened against her back, Chalcie and the horse were able to negotiate the thickening maze of pines and cedars.

Chalcie shivered. She could feel the effects of the poisoned stew she had been forced to eat. Her vision was beginning to blur, and her mouth felt funny. There was a dry sensation inside, as if she'd stuffed her cheeks with cotton. Her lips were prickling and then became numb as the poison began to work its way through her system.

"Oh God, please don't let me have eaten enough to make me go unconscious. I'll never make it down the hill, and they'll find me under some damn tree, frozen stiff, if anyone even notices that I'm gone," she said miserably. Her body might be eaten by the cougars or coyotes before spring had a chance to uncover her.

Her head ached and her stomach hurt. She wasn't certain how much was caused by the stew and how much from shock. She still wasn't sure that she and the horse would ever reach civilization, but even if she died of exposure, she'd have the satisfaction of having outsmarted Ames and Houlihan.

"I've got to make it. I'm not going to just give up and die on the side of this mountain," she said again, but reality was already beginning to blur around the edges. Was that a figure down in the brush or a tree? Where were the wolves that she heard howling? She didn't know there were wolves in the area…she'd have to tell people when she got back home. Or could it be the coyotes already on her trail, waiting for fresh warm meat to make their evening meal? She slumped forward against the mare.

The clouds had settled around the mountaintops. The gray and black blended, giving an eerie ghostlike appearance to the landscape. As she descended even farther below the timberline, Chalcedony began to chill as snowflakes sifted over her. She should have taken the smelly old bearskin, she thought dazedly. At least that would have given her some protection. But she had wanted to get away.

In the distance it seemed she could hear gunshots and the sounds of voices. In her half world of snow and dreams, she thought Ames and Houlihan were after her. She hadn't killed them, she had only slowed them down.

The dreams became brighter and more vivid as she slipped in and out of consciousness. She could feel the horse's warmth against her front, and wished she could find a comfortable way to lie against the animal without falling off. She awakened several times just as she was about to slide off into the darkness.

Aeons later, she felt the snow whip against her face.

"I smell smoke, don't you?" she whispered to the mare. Wherever the horse was headed as she stepped through the brambles and trees, she was working toward home and food. Chalcie could almost smell the sharp aroma of boiled coffee in the air.

"Dreaming again…" she mumbled as she heard a whistle and a voice in the darkness. The mare turned and stumbled slightly. It was just enough to break Chalcie's hold, and she finally let go, landing in a heap in the snow. It felt so warm, so comforting. Soft, she could sleep there forever. She knew what was happening, but she couldn't make herself get up. It was too much effort to move a muscle and push herself up and back onto the horse. Even the thought

of Ames and Houlihan after her couldn't cause enough of
a burst of energy to keep her going.

She didn't awaken when a gloved hand shook her
roughly, nor did she hear the soft steady stream of curses
from the man's lips.

"I'll be damned if I'm going to let you die of exposure.
Come on, wake up and fight."

Jordan hauled her out of the snow, slapping at her face
and rubbing her hands to give her warmth. The thin cotton
dress was slick with snow and stuck to her skin. If he tore
it off, great patches of her skin would be removed, too.
Time—there wasn't enough time. Gently he laid her on the
wool-and-fur blanket he had set out for his own bed that
night. He hoped it would be warm enough. He had been
hunting through the hills since the day after Estelle had
seen Chalcie kidnapped. He and Juanita had searched everywhere near Sonora, desperate to find Chalcie before
Ames harmed her. It was only reasonable that Ames had
kidnapped Chalcie in order to gain the inheritance. Jordan
thought about Ames, and a white-hot fire coursed through
him. If he'd done this to Chalcie, he was going to die for
it!

It was only in the last day that he had finally remembered
the old cabin that Houlihan used to talk about, and the
thought had occurred to him that Chalcie might be a pris-
oner there.

But he hadn't been prepared to find a half-frozen Chalcie
on the trail.

"Oh, God, what am I going to do?" he breathed as he
looked down at Chalcie. He had seen men like this, the
unlucky ones who had stayed out too long on their claim
and had finally come in, only to die. Gangrene could eat
away at the frozen fingers and dead white skin.

There was only one thing he could do.

"Now don't get any ideas, Chalcie. This isn't meant to
be anything other than a way to save your life. It's not that
I want you in my bed, but I can't stand to see Ames win,

and he will do exactly that if you die. Chalcie, can you hear me?''

Jordan reached down and touched the discolored area around her lips. It was bloody and bruised and he wondered what could have left those marks on her face. He looked again and saw the imprint of a fist in the bruises. Ames had beaten her, then. He was surprised by the flash of blinding fury that shook him and then subsided. He could take it out on Ames's hide later. Right now he had other things to worry about.

There was a flicker of life in Chalcie's body, but it was fading fast. She needed warmth, and lots of it. They were eight hours from town, and it was too dark to travel. It had been sheer blind luck that he'd heard the horse tracking downhill, and even more luck that she had answered to his shrill whistle and the rattle of a nose bag full of oats. And now that he had found Chalcie, he wasn't sure he could save her.

Chalcie shivered convulsively. She turned instinctively toward Jordan, seeking his warmth. She hurt. Her head ached and she couldn't shake the feeling that she was too far back in a cave to find her way out and see light again. She heard a voice and knew that it was a friend, but there was no face or name to go with the identification.

Jordan felt her body quaking as he held her. There was only one thing that he might be able to do to save her. He had known it from the moment the woman had slid off the horse and into the snow in front of him. She'd hate him when she woke up, if she ever did, but there was no helping that. Hell, she hated him anyway. She was so convinced that all he ever wanted out of her was the prime street property or the Kent fortunes that she'd never given him a chance to prove otherwise.

''Well, damned either way,'' he muttered, and began to strip the clothing from Chalcie's body. Even those few minutes in the blanket had warmed the cloth enough to break the icy grip on her skin. The flesh underneath the cotton and canvas was still pink and wet. There was a cold rough patch on her leg that had turned hard and white, and two of her toes looked bad. Considering what she had just survived, she was lucky if those were the only ill effects she suffered. He had to undress her and then warm her with his own body heat. Otherwise she would die. And he knew with a horrible certainty that if she lived and found out he'd taken her to bed, naked, flesh to flesh, she'd hate him for having compromised her.

If he didn't stop putting off the inevitable, she was going to die.

Jordan tipped the hot coffee he had been drinking onto his handkerchief and laid it across the white patch on her leg. The cloth cooled almost instantly in the frigid air, but the residual heat might save at least some of the skin.

Jordan finished the bed he'd started to make for himself. He'd laid the pine boughs into a mattress of sorts and covered the sharp prickles with an old piece of canvas that reached across the boughs and over a jutting branch to make a shelter. He had a wool blanket lined with soft wolves' fur that he had bought years back and still used when he traveled in the cold. He knew from past expeditions that it would keep him warm and comfortable in the snow. He pulled the canvas even tighter, breaking the chill of the wind.

Jordan kept up a steady running conversation to take his mind off the naked woman stretched out in front of him. He looked at her and was a little embarrassed by the tightening that he felt. She was in need of warmth, not lovemaking.

Memories played tricks with him, though, forcing him to remember how beautiful she'd been the night that she'd come to him in her fancy dress and Chinese shoes and her hair like a golden-red crown around her head. He had been so tempted to take her up on the offer of allowing her to buy the land in return for the chance to court her. But he'd never had to buy or barter for his women and he wasn't about to try. Besides, he'd always thought that eventually she would come back to him of her own accord, and they could start over if she really wanted him to court her. He hadn't thought the whole thing through or he would have known that she would have gone to hell and back before she would have let him near her again. When he'd laughed at her, he'd never realized that he was trampling her heart and making her hate him. He couldn't count the number of times he'd berated himself for being an insensitive oaf. He'd watched her walk down the streets, talk to other people and keep an icy, sullen indifference toward him. There was no way to mend the damage that had been done. If only he hadn't turned her down. If only he hadn't made her think that when he kissed her it had been because he wanted to be first in line to marry her for the estate. Somehow, when it came to Chalcie, it seemed as if the only thing he thought was, "If only I hadn't..."

He'd never be able to make it up to her.

"Unless you'll count saving your life as some kind of atonement," Jordan said quietly. "Hang on, Chalcie, it's almost done."

Jordan began to strip off his own clothes with methodical precision. The coat first, still warm from his body heat, to cover her up. Then his two shirts and the flannel-lined trousers, and finally he was down to the Indian-style lace-up boots that he preferred for wilderness riding.

Chalcie's eyes fluttered open. She felt almost warm, and there was a curious silky feeling under her back, almost as if she were lying on something soft and wonderful, instead of jolting down the hillside on the back of a horse. She focused on the figure above her and smiled. It was a dream of course. She had fallen off the horse and died and the coyotes had a meal of her. And now there was an angel there to welcome her to heaven, and he was naked. Very naked and very masculine, and he looked like Jordan. She liked angels who looked like Jordan. They would be friendly and warm and they'd smile at her. She opened her eyes wider in mild surprise. She'd never dreamed that angels came fully equipped and wearing Indian boots.

She raised her arms to him and then closed her eyes as she felt his wonderful warmth invade every inch of her body.

"God a'mighty, you're cold," Jordan swore softly as he slid under the pile of clothes and lay against her. He pulled the blanket of fur around her, making certain that she was protected from the wind and the lash of the sleet and snow. He was glad for its ample dimensions, remembering only now that the man he'd bought it from had said it was for two people.

"Let me hold you, Chalcie. I'll keep you safe and warm," he whispered as he pulled her close, giving her the warmth and rest that she craved.

He shouldn't be doing this, but there wasn't anything else he could do to keep her alive.

"I hope you understand…" he said as he snuggled close to her. In the distance he could hear the howl of the coyotes and the dull thud of the snow falling from the trees and hitting the ground.

He lay awake, listening and thinking.

What had she just gone through? From the look of the bruises around her mouth, she'd been beaten. He had run his hand over her hair a little while ago and found places on her scalp where the hair had been almost torn from the roots. There was matted blood all over the back of her head. He had had a good look at her body, and there didn't seem to be any other apparent bruises, but that didn't mean that she hadn't been mistreated.

Damn those men to eternity. If they were alive, he'd form a posse and the men would skin them and then stake them out and let them freeze to death. No one treated women like that, particularly not in the gold country. Women were precious, rare, to be cared for above all others.

Someday she'd have to talk about what had happened to

her. But not now. Right now he was going to cradle her and pretend that she was his, and that she had forgiven him for his refusal to court her.

Gingerly he held her in his arms, feeling the length of her body against his. It was utterly innocent, and he had never been so aroused in his life. What was it about this woman that could make him react like this? He had never felt this way before, even with the most exciting of women in the fandango parlors. Had she witched him the same way that her father witched gold out of the ground?

He shook his head at his fantasies.

He moved even closer to her and was rewarded by a soft sigh of contentment from Chalcie.

Chapter Ten

When Jordan awoke the next morning, his first confused impression was that he had been dreaming. He was at home in his own bed, and he'd been fantasizing about Chalcie. The feel of the skin like silk against his and the prod of Chalcie's firm breasts against his chest quickly dispelled that impression. Quietly he checked her respiration rate and felt the steady beating of her heart against the palm of his hand. He had a fleeting urge to yell in exultation. Chalcie was alive, she was breathing normally, and she was warm!

He'd done what he set out to do. He'd saved her life and he'd managed to keep his animal lusts under control. He could take her back to Sonora and she could get on with running the Kent fortunes, if that was what she wanted. Someone would marry her and she'd inherit it all, if she managed to make some kind of pact with the miners before the vows were said for return of all her property.

Jordan shifted slightly and was suddenly, embarrassingly aware that his body was having quite another response to Chalcie. A rush of passion had made him rise to the point, ready to make love to her on a moment's notice. Her skin was soft and warm, her hair smelled of smoke and fresh air, and her breasts teased against his chest.

"Damn," he groaned. His body was betraying him. It wasn't fair. He could have any woman he wanted in the fandango parlors, and with no strings attached. They were women who understood that a night in bed with them didn't mean that he wanted to spend the rest of his life with them. They understood him and his needs. Chalcie was different. She'd expect something from him if he bedded her, and he didn't need complications in his life. But there she was, a real complication, and his body wanted to take advantage of her.

There was only one way out of the mess, and that was to get up and dress and head back to Sonora as soon as possible.

Once he was dressed, he'd wake Chalcie up. He didn't want to startle her. She had been through enough danger and excitement. But the sooner they were on the trail back to Sonora, the better. He was as aware of the time limitation that her father had imposed on her legacy as she was.

Then, as he moved to withdraw from the warmth of the fur-lined blanket, he felt her stretch and she awakened.

"Where am I? Did I make it to heaven?" Chalcie murmured as she heard Jordan's voice. She tried to open her eyes and look around her to see what heaven was like. She managed to pry one eye open, but her vision was still blurred and unfocused. But the man who lay with his body against her certainly looked like Jordan de Chatain. Why was she hearing his voice and seeing his face in front of her? Shouldn't she have been seeing someone more dignified and upright in heaven? She felt him push against her and realized that there might be people more dignified in heaven, but few of them would be more upright.

She even remembered every moment of that ridiculous dream. Angels that looked like Jordan de Chatain—a naked Jordan de Chatain! How could a man that she hated have had such am impact on her? She shouldn't have been dreaming about him instead of a real angel.

Chalcie tried to force her eyes open again. She felt so comfortable, and there were none of the rancid sweaty smells of the cabin that she had awakened to for the past six days. If she could just look around, she could find out where she was. Strange that she'd be warm, when the last thing she remembered was falling off the horse into the snowbank. And that dream! If she opened her eyes, she could see if the dream had been so silly after all. But everything still had a quality of sleep about it. Nothing, not even the feel of a man's body against hers, was real yet. It couldn't be Ames who was holding her, she comforted herself. Ames was dead from the mushroom poison. He'd never have been able to escape from the cabin and come after her. It wasn't really a man's body; it probably had something to do with dying and going to heaven, where it was snug and smelled of man and wood smoke and fresh snow.

For now, though, she could indulge in the fantasy that she was safe in Jordan's arms.

Safe? Jordan? The two words should never even be put together in the same sentence!

Slowly she managed to bring both eyes into focus at the same time, opening first her right eye and then finally her left. She looked upward, staring directly into his deep black eyes. Until that very moment it had all been a dream, something that had no reality except in the fog-enshrouded recesses of her brain.

This, however, was not a dream.

Jordan! Like a million nerve endings firing, she felt him, all of him, in his upright masculine glory. Her breasts tightened at the touch of his chest hair. She felt his manhood pressing against her legs, urging her to open them and give herself to him.

Oh my God, she thought, stunned. How could she have come to this? She had just escaped Ames and Houlihan and had ended up in another man's bed?

Chalcie moaned softly as her whole body ached in a spasm of sheer desire. She had never known what it was like to lie with a man and enjoy it. She had never even thought of such a thing.

The only thing she knew for certain about making love was that the women in the parlors made a great deal of money by their actions, and that most ''proper'' women thought that marital duties were dirty. Could this wonderful wanting have been what they meant? And if so, how stupid of them to hate it!

She tried to think about the humiliation of Jordan's laughter the day she had offered herself to him, but even that was met with a certain apathy. Too much had happened in the last few days for her to be angered over such a silly thing.

For the first time she realized just what she had done, against all odds—she had survived.

She had beaten Ames and left him for dead. The amanita spared no one once the mushrooms had been eaten in the quantities that Houlihan and Ames had consumed. She had ridden down the mountain and had survived the snowstorm. She had not frozen to death, even though she knew instinctively that Jordan had made her survive the freezing weather by pressing his naked skin against her. The very thought of his actions heated her body and her blood. She remembered other stories about men in wartime who had wanted nothing more than to make love after they'd faced death. She felt like those men. She wanted to hold Jordan and have him caress her. She wanted Jordan. She had never wanted anything more in her life than she wanted to make love to Jordan right then and there.

Slowly, almost unconsciously, she began to move her hips, rotating against his body. It felt so good, so right. She was aware of everything. Jordan's throbbing response to her movement, the way her breasts were tight and ready to be touched, the urgency of her need to have him make love to her all swept her away with desperate need.

Jordan was content to hold Chalcie in his arms until she started to move her hips. She was innocent and seductive, vibrant with unfulfilled passion and dangerous as all hell.

There was a moment when Jordan allowed himself to

respond to her. He could have been swept away with the rising passions and later pleaded that he hadn't really been awake. He wanted her. There was fire and promise in her that could have brought him to an answering fever.

"No, Chalcie, it would be all wrong," he said aloud, firmly. No matter that he had thought about just this scene when he'd watched her going about her daily routine in Sonora. No matter that he'd wished a thousand times over that he could have recalled his cruel laugh and his taunting words when he told her he didn't want a wife. Then he had refused to help her with the land and had fallen even further in his own estimation. He didn't need to add seducing her to the list of terrible things he'd done to Chalcie Kent. He wasn't going to take advantage of her until she knew exactly what she was doing.

Turning away from her was the most difficult thing he had ever done. Only the shock of the icy snow-laden wind on his bare bottom made it possible to think clearly. He had saved her, but that didn't mean she owed him her maidenhood out of gratefulness.

Chalcie looked up at him, her eyes beginning to blur with tears. He looked so fine and beautiful standing there naked, just like her dream last night. She wanted him more than anything she had ever wanted in her life, and he refused to make love to her.

Jordan saw the look and for a moment his resolve wavered. She wanted it. What could be the harm in giving in?

"Because she'd hate you," he answered himself regretfully. He reached down and pulled his pants and shirt from the fur blanket, where they'd been tangled around them as they slept.

"Chalcie, I'm sorry…believe me, more sorry than you'll ever know. But I can't do that to you. Not now. Not here," Jordan said. Taking a deep breath, he ignored her sad blue eyes and her distress. "Hurry up and dress while I feed the horses and clean up. We have to get back to Sonora."

Chalcie stared at him, confusion and hurt transparent on

her face. Silently she sat up, using what she could grab of the blanket to cover herself.

Jordan looked at her and almost sat back down on the fur. Just one movement and he could tumble her into his arms. Her red hair fell in a splendid tangle of curls around her face and shoulders. Her eyes were dark with pain, and he longed to see her generous mouth smile just once as she had smiled up at him when they were cuddled close together. The blanket parted for a moment, revealing a flash of breasts that made Jordan gasp with the sudden desperate need for release. He couldn't ever remember wanting a woman so much and still denying himself the pleasure of her body.

Chalcie turned away from him.

Damn it, she'd made a fool of herself again. He had wanted her, she knew he had. He'd been just as excited as she was, and then he'd moved away from her. She'd offered herself to him and he'd turned her down, just like the first time. Only this time she hadn't been dressed in a fancy linen dress. She'd been naked and warm and wanton, and he still turned his back on her.

Chalcie was mortified that he still didn't want her. Of course she should have known, she silently berated herself. He never had liked her. She didn't know why he had been riding up the trail, but it certainly had had nothing to do with her. And if it did, it was only because he'd come searching for her to win a chance to marry her and get the land and businesses for free. He knew as well as she did that if she didn't marry in the next twenty-four hours, she would have to walk away from it all and start over.

She could go back to Boston, to the life that her father had stolen her from. She'd have to work her way east; there would be no free passage back to her grandmother's house. And once she arrived she knew that she would have to live through hell until she managed to find a way to fit back into polite society.

An involuntary sob rose in her throat. Go back to Boston? She would never manage to fit into the whalebone rigid beliefs of her grandmother and grandfather. Better to find someone to marry and be done with it. When Jordan had rescued her last night, she had dreamed—wished—that Jordan would be the man to take pity on her and marry her. Jordan would have control of the land. That was what he wanted most. That way, even if it was a marriage in name only, she could have continued to live in California.

"It's not fair," she whispered as she looked out over the gleaming new snow that coated the mountains. They were blue, almost black with the distance, and a haze shimmered around the mountain peaks. From far off she could hear the scream of a hawk on the wing, flying free. She could marry Jordan, if he'd have her, but she'd never have what she wanted most—the approval of her father and a husband who really loved her.

Her father had taken away any chance she would ever have of being free, and there wasn't a man in all of Sonora who would look at her as anything other than a way to instant riches.

Jordan lingered over rolling up the blankets, wondering at his own motivation. He'd never refused a willing, attractive woman before. He reached for the smaller blanket and threw it at Chalcie. She was standing to one side, trying not to shiver as the wind cut through her thin cotton dress. Jordan had the uncomfortable feeling that if he hadn't remembered that she needed something to keep her warm, she would have mounted the mare and ridden back to town with nothing between her and the storm but the calico.

"Wear that blanket. I'm not going to have my life-saving skills questioned by letting you freeze on the ride back," Jordan said shortly.

Chalcie nodded and wrapped the blanket around her. She was so cold that she could gladly have ridden wrapped in the fur one, but she wasn't about to ask for that kind of favor from Jordan. She didn't want to give him yet another reason to turn her down.

Jordan led the way down the mountain. He was careful not to look at Chalcedony. He could see the hurt and anger in her eyes, but he had no intention of trying to make things better.

He was uncomfortably aware of the physical attraction between the two of them. He had only to think about her breasts against his chest and that slow movement against his manhood to be instantly, throbbingly erect. He wanted her physically, but that wasn't enough to base a lifelong relationship on. She was a spitfire, ready to fight for anything and everything she felt she deserved. He'd never thought of marriage as a battleground, but it would be with her unless she allowed him to love her and she returned his love.

"Love?" He frowned and tasted the word as he said it quietly.

He had no idea why the word had popped into his mind, but it certainly didn't bear any relationship to what he felt for Chalcedony Kent. Lust maybe, but not love. He'd get her back to Sonora and drop her off, and she would be on her own after that.

But the word rang in his mind—*love*. Could it possibly be true? The strange thing was, he wanted more than her luscious body. He realized, wonderingly, that he wanted to hold her and soothe away all the troubles that had filled her life. He wanted to make her feel secure and happy. If he did all of that for her, then she would love him in return, wouldn't she?

But what if she never learned to love him?

Jordan shrugged his shoulders. It was all a dream, anyway. He had rescued her and kept her alive and nothing more was going to happen between them.

Chalcedony watched the silent figure in front of her. She was achingly aware of the way he sat on the horse, of the way he handled the reins. Those hands had touched her this morning and their awakening force had been more than she had ever dreamed possible. Men had touched her before,

mostly in jest when she worked in the bar. But nothing, not
even the furtive kisses she had stolen with several of the
younger men in town, had caused her body to react with
such fierce need.

"Settle down," she told herself firmly. He didn't want
her, he'd made that much clear. She would simply have to
find another man and marry him. Surely she could manage
to find one love-starved miner in a town of several hundred
who would be willing to marry her and give her back control of her own holdings.

"Chalcedony?"

Jordan stopped the horses as they topped the rise.

"Yes, Jordan?" She waited hopefully.

"I just wanted to tell you that I didn't confide in anyone
except Juanita about going after you. In fact, no one except
me knows for certain that you were kidnapped. There were
rumors, but most of the men didn't think much about your
disappearing for a while. After all, you did it a couple of
months ago. And then, with your father just murdered—
well, they thought you were sequestered after your father's
death…in mourning, you know."

Chalcedony looked at him blankly.

"No, I don't know," she said, wondering what this was
all about.

Jordan slapped the reins against his hand in exasperation.
She couldn't be that naive!

"Chalcie, if you'd been taken against your will, then
they'd also think you might have been…" His voice trailed
off and a blush mounted underneath his tan. Maybe he
should have talked to her about what had happened on the
mountain with Ames and Houlihan. But he had been so
wrapped up in his thoughts about her desires and his need
that he hadn't even bothered to make certain that Chalcedony had not, indeed, been raped.

Oh God, if they'd done that to her, he'd kill them. The
thought cut through him like an icy knife.

"Chalcie, they didn't?"

Chalcie blushed. "They did nothing. I cleaned the cabin and cooked their meal and Ames talked about marrying me and then murdering me. I don't think he wanted to sully his reputation by actually…bedding me." She could barely get the words out. She turned her face away from Jordan, ashamed even to be talking about such things with a man. Suddenly it dawned on Chalcedony what Jordan had been hinting about. The men in the camp would have the same questions about her.

"You mean the men will think I've been raped? Used by those foul excuses for men?" She shuddered.

Jordan shrugged uncomfortably.

"Don't you think someone is going to put it together when they see me riding in on Ames's mare?" she asked acidly. It didn't matter what the truth was, she knew what the men would believe. Jordan was right. All the careful plans she had made about getting married to the first man who would give her back the Kent holdings were collapsing. She might be able to find a man who would accept her as a wife, but it would be difficult. The double standard of what the miners expected of women was just as crazy in California as it was anywhere else.

The only men who would have her now might be the ones who wanted the fortune and nothing else. No one would want her for herself, for the woman she was and for the wife she could be. They'd think of her as a sullied woman. And they would never give her back the Kent fortune. They'd think the money and land were only fair payment for taking in a woman who had been defiled.

"I'll take the horse, and you walk from the edge of town. Can you manage that?" Jordan had it all planned. There wouldn't be even the smallest hint of impropriety.

"Of course I can," she answered. Chalcedony gritted her teeth against the anger and despair that surged through her.

"Tell me, what made you come after me, if you didn't want me…?" To her shame, Chalcie heard her voice break at the end of the question.

Jordan sighed. He'd been waiting for the question and hoping that she wouldn't ask it.

"I heard your father boasting about that will, and all I could think about was the trouble it was going to cause you. I had already warned you. I figured that I'd done my duty by telling you about the will, since it was damn clear that your father wasn't about to tell you the terms he'd set up. Then someone came running into the saloon yelling about James Kent being shot." Jordan wished he could think of some way to soften the words, but there weren't any delicate and genteel ways to talk about her father being gunned down in the middle of the street.

"I couldn't figure out why Ames would shoot him, so I started asking questions. There were men there who'd heard a fight brewing between your father and Ames. Seems there were several men just itching to let your father know about Ames's reputation back in San Francisco. The man had quite a history of coming in, bleeding people of everything and then moving on to the next victim. He'd figured on playing your father the same way. I don't know what made the difference, why they were willing to step forward now instead of coming forward earlier, but the will naming Ames as the person to get everything seemed to have something to do with it. You're pretty well liked and the men thought it was a shame what your father was doing to you."

Jordan slowed the horses as they turned downhill again. For the first time, they could see the smoke from the town rising in the wind.

"They convinced my father that Ames was out to cheat him?"

"Evidently they convinced your father that Ames was trying some kind of slippery deal. When it dawned on your father what he had almost done to you, he started making noise about ripping up the will and starting over again, fresh."

Chalcie closed her eyes. The huge knot of grief and anger that she had felt inside since she heard about the will and her father's death slowly eased. So that was how it had happened. Her father hadn't abandoned her, then. He had finally thought about the impact of his actions on her.

"Obviously, Ames wasn't about to allow your father to rip up the will. It was his passport to the Kent fortune, just in case he couldn't get it away from the old man while he was still alive. So he shot him."

Chalcie shuddered to hear the words from someone else. If she had ever had any qualms about poisoning Ames, they were resolved with that sentence. She was glad that she had at least partially avenged her father's murder. She would have liked it better, though, if the men had suffered more before they died. It had been too easy on them after all the suffering they had inflicted on her family.

She focused on Jordan's last words about the will being ripped up.

Chalcie brightened. "Then I'm safe. I don't have to worry about the will?"

Jordan cleared his throat, wishing he didn't have to tell her the truth. "No, that's not quite right. Your father didn't have a chance to nullify the will. It's still written in black and white, and the paper is being kept at Mary's saloon. You are still bound by the terms of it."

"Then I'd better get busy, hadn't I?" Chalcie said tightly. She had some work ahead of her before the clock struck twelve tonight. She wasn't going to marry Ames, because he was dead, and she wasn't going to walk away and build another life unless she was forced to. That left her with the job of finding a husband who wanted her and not just her money.

It was late afternoon when they finally turned toward the muddy main street of Sonora. Chalcedony dismounted and gave the reins of Ames's mare to Jordan. She threw the blanket over the saddle. Without looking back, she started slogging across the street. She shivered from the cold and fright, wishing desperately that she could be back in the fur blanket, with Jordan's body pressed against hers.

She didn't see Jordan reaching out involuntarily to hold her back, to bring her back to him so he could ask her to marry him. She saw nothing but the dismal road ahead and the prospect of hunting for someone who might be able to learn to love her.

"Well, he did it, then. He managed to save you," Juanita greeted her as she walked into the smoky warmth of the bar. One quick look told her that the girl was dead on her feet and probably suffering from shock. She knew that Jordan had intended to allow Chalcedony to walk back into town on her own to try to silence rumors about where she had been.

When he had said that he was going out to try to find her at Houlihan's cabin, they had discussed what he should do to ensure that the men in the town never knew for certain whether she'd been alone with Ames and Houlihan or had simply gone off to mourn her father in private.

What Jordan didn't know was that in the past day the rumors had been whispered and then shouted—James Kent had been murdered and Chalcedony had ridden away with his murderers.

The miners would judge the men who had compromised her harshly, but Chalcedony's reputation was also in tatters. She was soiled goods now, the kind of woman that no decent man would want to marry unless he had an eye only for her gold.

Juanita grabbed Chalcedony's arm and pulled her through the curtain and around to her own room.

"Did Jordan say he'd marry you?" she asked. There was no time for preliminaries. All the men knew that this was the last day of the week, and there wasn't a marriageable male in sight for the girl.

Chalcedony shook her head miserably. They'd talked about what the men would think, but he hadn't offered marriage and she hadn't expected it.

"My God, he's got to know what the men will say now

that you're back in town.... There's been talk already. He's the only man who would be able to face down those starched-shirt priss pots out there. They all think you're a fallen woman now. Didn't he want you?''

Juanita was furious with the man. Stupid—she'd seen the way he looked at Chalcie, and it was love if she'd ever seen it. Yet he'd sent her back to face the men of Sonora without even offering Chalcie the possibility of marriage with him.

Yes, Chalcie thought, he'd wanted something, but not exactly her. Most likely it had been a passing lust. Nothing that she could explain to Juanita.

''It doesn't matter,'' Chalcie began. ''Besides, Ames tried but he didn't manage to carry through what he wanted. I'm still pure, if that's what you're concerned about.''

Juanita snorted. ''Men are funny that way. They'll turn you down because you might have been raped when you were twelve and you couldn't do anything about it. Then they'll marry a woman from the fandango parlor without batting an eye and make her into an honest woman. But they'll never forgive you the idea that you might, just might have been used before by a man if you're supposed to be a good woman. And that leaves us with the only men who will marry you—the ones who don't care about you but want the money.''

''Well, if it's not going to be a man who wants me for myself, and it's not a man who wants just the money, who the hell does that leave?''

''Jordan.''

''I'd rather die,'' Chalcie said.

Juanita ignored her. ''I know that man and I know that he is going to make you a good husband, and you're going to be a wonderful wife for him. We just have to convince him to see it our way.''

''I will not! I wouldn't be a wife to him if he was the last man on earth,'' Chalcie exploded. Her head ached and she wanted to cry.

"Well, he might as well be the last man, for all the chance you'll have of marrying before your father's deadline. Don't fight me, girl, I know what I'm doing. Get changed into the linen dress. It'll serve as a wedding dress."

Chalcie shook her head violently. "I'm not marrying Jordan and I'm certainly not going to go see anyone wearing a dress that I was wearing when I asked for help and was turned down flat."

Juanita sighed. Chalcie was right. She couldn't go back to Jordan wearing the same dress, and there wasn't time to make another one.

"Your velvet! That'll be perfect. It's cold enough now, and the blue with your red hair will make you look like a real bride instead of a woman desperate to save herself."

Chalcie shook her head.

"Give it up, Juanita. I'm not going to get married. I'm not going to stay here and run the Kent properties. It's all going to go to the miners, and I'm going to move on."

"But what will you do? How can it possibly be better to walk away from it all instead of giving Jordan a chance to do right by you?"

"Why should he?" Chalcie asked bitterly. "He had a chance to make love to me if he'd wanted to…" Her hand flew to her mouth. She hadn't meant to tell Juanita about that!

Juanita smiled slowly. There, that was what she needed. She didn't know what kind of game Jordan was playing, but if he'd almost made love to Chalcie, that meant there was some hope. It might not be love, but lust wouldn't hurt a bit.

"We'll just give him another chance, now won't we?" Juanita wasn't going to let Chalcie leave. She was the best boss a woman had ever had and she was a friend. A friend was hard to come by in the gold country and she didn't even want to think of Sonora without her. And to make certain that Chalcie stayed, she had to get her married off to Jordan before midnight.

Chalcie needed a bath and then she needed a new dress.

Quickly Juanita enlisted the aid of the other women in the bar. The brand-new copper tub that served as a bath if the men were willing to pay an ounce of gold for it was brought to Chalcie's room. Steaming water from the stove was poured in.

"Now, slide down in that and soak, and I'll be right back," Juanita ordered.

Chalcie followed the orders. She was too tired and depressed even to begin to object. The heated water lapped gently over her, soothing the cold ache that had ridden with her since that morning. She picked up the soap and towel Juanita had left. Sweet-smelling lather brought her further back into the world of the living. She soaked for a few minutes and then she rinsed herself one last time. She was numb and exhausted and too damned tired to fight. Let Juanita have her way. She'd soon discover that Jordan wanted no part of her and the fine Kent fortune.

When the water finally began to cool, Chalcedony climbed out and wrapped herself in the old cotton blanket Juanita had left on the rocking chair. The tears that had been threatening all day began to seep out. She was so tired she couldn't move another foot, and she didn't care whether she managed to marry anyone or not. It was already completely dark outside, and she knew that there were only a few more hours. She didn't care. She couldn't face the men; she couldn't ask any of them to marry her. It was simply too much. She'd go to Murphys to the new find or she'd go back to Boston and leave the whole damn state to the miners.

"Here, put this on." Juanita threw a bundle of cloth at Chalcie.

"What?" Chalcie caught the bundle and shook out the dress of fine light cream satin with handmade lace edging.

She looked from the dress to Juanita, and the woman's dark eyes glanced away guiltily.

"Juanita, I can't—this was your wedding dress!" Chalcedony said. She knew what the dress meant to Juanita. Her friend never even wore light colors anymore. When she fancied herself up for a night at the bar, she wore deep reds and greens, good colors to brighten a miner's day. The rich velvets complemented her dark skin and black hair. But she never wore white satin.

"But it's yours," Chalcie said in confusion.

"I'll never wear it again. I don't want to be married, Chalcie. You know that. No one could ever be as good as my sainted Miguel. But this dress is perfect for you tonight. You need it."

"Don't forget Eduardo, Juanita. You're going to need this for him. I do have the velvet."

"Yes, you do. But for the wedding, no matter what you think about it, you need a dress with romance, something to make you feel beautiful. This dress can do that. Look at the lace, feel the satin. Think of it against your skin and with your red hair. Jordan will never be able to resist you."

Chalcie didn't point out that he had already resisted her several times and she was probably setting herself up for another rejection.

Juanita knew what Chalcie was thinking. But it would work this time. It had to. Chalcie would make a beautiful romantic bride and it was Juanita's firmly held belief that if the marriage started off with romance, it would endure with love.

Chalcedony looked down at the dress. It deserved to be worn by a woman who was going to the altar happily, secure in the knowledge that she would be cherished. She knew that no matter what happened, that wouldn't be true for her. Necessity, desperation and greed—those would stand up for her at the marriage, like silent men of dishonor behind her.

"Put it on, we don't have much time."

Chalcedony donned the dress. Juanita pulled her hair back into a sleek chignon that gleamed dull red in the lamplight. Her natural color was so pink that she didn't need an artful touch of wet red flannel to make her look perfect.

"It won't make any difference, you know. Jordan won't marry me and there's no one else," Chalcie said sadly.

"Trust me," Juanita said again. Her face was a grim mask.

"Where are we going?" She really didn't care, but obviously Juanita had something planned.

"To Jordan's house," Juanita answered.

Chalcedony looked at her in horror. Hadn't Juanita heard a thing she'd said in the last few hours? Asking Jordan to marry her was impossible.

Juanita saw her expression and shook her head. "Not a word. I'll deal with that man once we get there," she said.

Chalcedony didn't have the heart or the strength to object.

The trek through the town was undertaken in silence, using the back road where no one would see her. Chalcie had pulled on the long flannel-and-wool coat that she had bought in San Francisco. It concealed most of the wedding dress. Juanita was ready to knock on the front door, when there was a sound from inside the house.

It looked, Chalcie thought miserably, like a home that needed a woman in it who was loved. It already had a man and a cat and a stove to keep warm. All it needed was a happy wife. But that wasn't going to be her, that was certain.

Jordan opened the door and stepped out onto the thick slab of red rock that served as his front porch. He had changed into clean clothes. With his hair tousled from the water and freshly shaved, he was the epitome of a good-looking man.

Unbidden, the thought of him pressed against her naked body came to Chalcie's mind. She shivered at the recollection. Oh, how she had wanted him!

He had turned her down.

Chalcie pivoted and started back down the path. She wasn't going to do this. The last ember of rebellion flared.

"I told you no, and I meant no. I don't need him and he doesn't need me," Chalcie declared as she tried to push past her friend.

"You need him. I agree that he doesn't need you, but he has a compassionate heart. He will see that you are well treated."

"Excuse me, ladies, might I say something?"

Both Chalcie and Juanita turned to stare at Jordan. They were stunned to see him grinning like a fool.

"Oh, good, I have your attention," he said.

He stepped down toward them, still smiling. He reached out and took Chalcie's hand in his own, and the shock of her skin against his made him even more certain that he was right. If they'd given him a few more minutes, he'd have met them at the saloon instead of making Chalcie trek all this way to his cabin. He pulled her closer to him and felt her reluctance as she tried to resist him.

Jordan noticed the shiver as she stared at him. It reminded him of a small bird about to be eaten alive. There was an expression of blank pain on her face that made him wince. He knew that she felt she'd been forced to come to him, when all he really wanted was for her to marry him and be happy. She wouldn't believe that he had been on his way down to the saloon to tell her that she had to marry him because he couldn't stand the thought of her married to anyone else.

Unbidden, another set of scenes flashed through his mind. Chalcie in the furs, moving against him. Chalcie naked and pink as he looked down on her. Chalcie as his wife, and the chance to give in to the almost unbearable need to make love to her.

He knew that she didn't love him now. But there was always the chance that she might fall in love with him. If she would only become his wife, then he'd have her all to himself. He couldn't stop thinking about the way she'd felt against him. It hadn't been the same as simple lust; it had been something more, something richer and more passionate.

He'd hoped that she would come to him with a smile, with the memory of the way their bodies had melded together. Then he could share everything with her, his body and his soul.

Finally, here she was, standing in front of him, and he felt a rush of delight when he looked at her. Then he saw her expression again and the joy left him as completely as if it had never been.

Chalcie had come looking like a woman being led to the gallows. She was expecting him to hurt her again.

Had he been so cruel to her? The answer, irrefutably, was yes.

He ached for the pain she must be feeling now. All that valiant fighting, all the brave words, and here she was, reduced to accepting a husband so she could keep what was rightfully hers to begin with. He'd been informed almost as soon as he'd stabled his horse that Chalcedony Kent was no longer a woman of good repute. Her chances for a decent marriage had gone to zero.

Juanita opened her mouth, but he silenced her with a gesture.

"No, Chalcie, you don't need to try and leave me again," he said, his voice low and soothing. "I only wanted to come home and change into better clothes before I came back to claim my prize."

"Your prize?" Chalcie asked, her eyes wide.

"My prize. I rescued you, I kept you alive, I slept with you. That means that I won a chance to make you my wife. Please give me a chance at winning your heart."

Chalcie almost fainted. Surely he couldn't mean this!

"You want to marry me?" she asked faintly.

"I want to marry you and have you as my wife and finally be able to make love to you," Jordan said simply.

Chalcie stood there and listened to the words, and as she listened, she began to feel her emotions beginning to thaw. Was it possible that he really did care for her? Had she misjudged him? She had been certain that he was only concerned with the money she would bring to the marriage. But when he talked about making love to her—or was it only lust?

She couldn't have everything. She'd settle for what she could get. The chance to be married to Jordan de Chatain was enough. Perhaps, if she was lucky, he'd fall in love with her later.

His heart ached for the pain she had endured, and he wanted to protect her. He would kiss that look from her eyes and taste her sweet mouth, and they'd start again, fresh. It would be a good marriage. He could make it good. It would take time before she realized that he could really love her. Jordan gently removed the coat to reveal the wedding dress. He marveled at her skin and the color in her cheeks. His body was playing tricks on him again as he thought about loosening her hair and lifting the dress over her head.

He hadn't even noticed that, in the space of the morning to the evening, he had gone from being certain that he could never love her to glad acceptance that he was going to have a chance to show her just how much he could love her.

Jordan leaned forward and kissed her lightly on the lips, shocking her with a sudden desire that made her sway against him.

"Chalcedony, will you marry me?"

Chapter Eleven

Chalcie leaned her forehead against the wall and closed her eyes in desperation.

"Forget it, Juanita, I can't go out there. I'd rather work my way back to Boston than force Jordan into marrying me."

"That wasn't what I saw when he asked you to marry him. I saw a man who looked at you as if he were being presented with the crown jewels."

"How apt. That's the truth, isn't it? It's the money, not me," Chalcie said.

Juanita threw up her hands in exasperation. Chalcie was determined to take everything she said the wrong way.

"I want to marry for love, even if I live like a poor woman for the rest of my life," Chalcie said desperately.

"Stop saying stupid things. You don't want to be poor again and we both know it. You sure as hell don't want to go back to Boston. Jordan's not such a bad person to be marrying. He'll do right by you," Juanita said, ignoring the wild look on Chalcie's face.

"I can't. It's like stage fright. I'm playing a part and I know that I'm not going to be any good in it."

Chalcie didn't add that she knew that tonight she'd have to give the most convincing performance of her life when she vowed to take Jordan as her husband. She looked out at the blur of faces that spilled out beyond the bar and into the street.

From her vantage point between the buildings in the alleyway, she could see that every miner in Sonora was in attendance, ready for the evening's entertainment. The bar had been cleared and polished. The red calico curtains at the front and one side had been pulled up out of the way so that the sea of miners could watch the marriage of Chalcedony Kent and Jordan de Chatain. The men hungered for excitement, and here it was, delivered—romance and all—to their doorstep. No one had ever expected the two enemies to wed, particularly now that Chalcedony was a soiled woman, fit only for the fandango parlors.

"Jordan's set it up so that there'll never be any question about your marriage. He's taking care of you, Chalcie. You'd better thank him for that. Otherwise you'd be broke at one minute after midnight. So shut up and get out there and get married," Juanita said in exasperation.

Chalcedony stood in the dark passage between her saloon and Jordan's fandango parlor. She couldn't face that crowd, no matter what she stood to lose. She had thought the marriage would be fast, simple and fake. It hadn't occurred to her that the miners would make a festival of the evening.

"You have to be properly married within the next ten minutes, and furthermore, you'd better have all the witnesses you can find to make certain the world knows you were married before the stroke of twelve. Now get on down there and wait for your groom. He'll be along shortly." Juanita gave her a firm shove across the narrow unlit alley that led to the saloon.

Chalcedony stumbled several steps, and then, deciding that anything was better than standing frozen with fear in the darkness, she walked toward the bar.

She was almost even with the office at the back of the fandango parlor when she heard voices, one Jordan's familiar deep baritone, the other of a stranger.

"Let me get it sorted out, Tourelle. I've got to get married first. I told you, I'll know how much I can afford to sell in a few days. I've got to decide how I'm going to divide everything up.''

Chalcedony's heart stopped in shock and then thudded painfully back to life. She would have fainted if she had been the fainting kind.

So her worst fears were to be realized. The marriage would take place and she would be stripped of everything she had ever worked for. Divide everything? Even her own property was going to be taken from her? Chalcie's hands closed convulsively. How could she win against someone like Jordan?

Damn you, Father, I hope you rot in hell for this, she thought. Her father had stolen more than he would ever realize. Not only would she lose the businesses, but she would never know love the way other women would. She would have nothing but dreams for the rest of her life. She didn't care that her father had tried to undo his foolishness—he hadn't succeeded, and it had ruined her life.

''No,'' she whispered as she stared at the bar twenty feet away from her. She saw her prized wall clock ticking away the seconds.

She knew she had to marry him, but that didn't make the action any easier.

Jordan approached from behind her. He caught her hand in his, a grip that, while not painful, was unbreakable.

''It's time. I know you're frightened, but trust me. It will be all right,'' he said, trying to soothe her.

The sound of his voice promising to break up the Kent fortune was too clear for her to believe him.

Jordan pulled her into the lighted area at the back of the saloon, and the miners began to cheer as they saw the pair advancing toward the bar. The preacher smiled as they neared him.

Jordan's stride did not falter as Chalcie held back, reluctant to see her fate so thoroughly sealed. If she had been

able to break away, she would have made a wild dash out
the door as her nerve broke.

But there's nothing to go to, she thought miserably. It
was this marriage or nothing. She had to go through with
it.

"That's the way, Jordan. Start out showing her who's
the boss!" Blackie Hardesty called out.

"Give it to her, Jordan. She needs a firm hand…" Henry
Stollen chimed in.

"And a firm…"

Blessedly the last comment was drowned out by the rising roar of approval from the crowd.

Chalcie's face was scarlet with embarrassment and anger.
Her carefully coiffed hair, pinned and braided into a crown
of deep red, was in danger of falling down around her
shoulders. She was terrified that she'd put a foot through
the fragile lace of Juanita's dress. The crowd surged around
her, and if she hadn't been protected by Jordan's arm, she
would have been knocked to the ground.

Some of the miners stepped in, trying to push the crowd
back so the marriage could take place.

"Brother de Chatain, I humbly suggest that we get on
with this. We don't have time for the fancy stuff." Rev-
erend Jamiston leaned toward the couple.

The shouting died down and the bar was quiet. There
was the sound of hundreds of feet shuffling as the men
craned for a better view, and somewhere near the back
someone was still whistling a wedding tune. The crowd
waited intensely to see if the two antagonists could beat
the deadline.

"Chalcie, do you take Jordan de Chatain for your husband, for now and forever?"

Chalcie looked up at Jordan, and his hand tightened
again around her wrist. There was no escape.

"I do."

Short, sweet and to the point. Jordan's hand dropped

away from her arm, and suddenly she felt bereft. At least it had been contact.

"Jordan, do you take Chalcedony Kent as your wife?"

"I do" rang out as the clock began to strike the first note of twelve midnight.

Jordan leaned down and kissed Chalcie, touching her lips as he had longed to do since waking up and finding her naked warmth pressed against him. She tasted sweet, and for just a moment, a passing second, he allowed himself to think that life with her could be equally sweet, if she'd just give him a chance to show her that they might fall in love after all.

Chalcie broke the kiss. She looked down at her hand, still bare of a ring, and turned away from him blindly. It was done. No matter how much she liked the kiss, she didn't have to pretend that it was anything more than a public show carefully planned and calculated by Jordan to prove to everyone that she was indeed his bride.

She wished that it was different. She wished that this marriage was real. But she had heard Jordan planning to break up the Kent fortune. He wasn't going to have her as a real wife. Instead, he was going to strip her bare of her money and move on to other women. She knew that he'd never bed her. He had already made that abundantly clear this morning. He could have had her, ready and willing, and he'd turned her down. Twice was enough for any woman. She'd never come to him again, wanting to be taken in his arms. He'd have her money but he would never have her heart.

There was a roar of approval as the kiss ended, and the miners began to applaud and stamp their feet as the couple separated. The men were as excited as if it were their own romantic wedding they were celebrating.

"Drinks on the house!" Juanita bustled up to the bar and began to set up the glasses. Paul, the mining camp's only fiddler, began to play a rousing dance tune to start the festivities.

''One dance and we're off to bed,'' Jordan said, and there was another roar of approval as he led Chalcie out to the small patch of floor that the men cleared.

They fitted together, Chalcie thought as he put his arms around her. She let herself drift into a dream in which he loved her and she would live with him happily forever and that this was her wedding dance, which she would remember as they grew old together. His arms touched the right places, his warmth against her made her almost faint with desire for more. She was aware of the slight pressure of her breasts against his chest and was wickedly delighted to hear him gasp as if breathing were difficult for him, too.

They moved slowly together, a decorous dance with his arms holding her like a fragile wildflower. It was all show, designed to make certain that no one had any funny ideas about the contract not being fulfilled.

To the miners they looked like the perfect couple. He was tall and darkly handsome, she was beautiful in the only wedding dress for a hundred miles around. Juanita wasn't the only one in the bar wiping away a surreptitious tear as the couple spun slowly to the strains of the violin. Eduardo stood beside her and put his arm around her shoulder.

''Maybe we will be next, if you'll have me,'' he said quietly.

Juanita nodded, knowing that she might finally have to put the memory of Miguel to rest and think about Eduardo as a life companion. The very thought frightened her to death.

''We're off,'' Jordan announced jovially as the dance ended. He drew Chalcie against him, holding her firmly around the waist in case she had any ideas about bolting.

''No, Jordan, you're on, if you're doing it right!'' one of the miners yelled as they left the saloon.

Jordan saluted them and walked into the darkness toward his house.

Neither of them broke the silence as they negotiated the treacherous path. Chalcie was desperately trying to mak sure that she didn't ruin Juanita's dress, and Jordan was trying to help her keep her balance in the mire left by the snowstorm.

"Jordan, when you're tired of Miss Fancy Pants, I'll still be here." One of the whores from the fandango parlor leaned out the window, her breasts bobbling beneath the thin cotton chemise that did nothing to cover her more than adequate attributes.

"If you want to work another night for me, Suzette, you'd better never insult my wife again," Jordan said, his voice pitched so that it would carry clearly to the second story.

Suzette looked down at her boss, her face a study of confusion and anger.

"I'm sorry, Chalcie, the women tend to get carried away sometimes."

"I'm not surprised that you've done what almost every man here does," Chalcie said slowly. She didn't add that the thought of him in bed with another woman made her stomach churn. From the sounds of it, Jordan had bedded almost every woman in Sonora.

An idea was beginning to take shape. She didn't want Jordan to think that she intended to be his wife in anything but name. They'd acted as if everything were going to be just fine that night, a normal night for any newlywed. But she'd be damned if she was actually going to let this man in her bed. She wasn't really married. Marriage for convenience didn't count. Someday she'd have more, and that would be the time for loving. But until then, she would stay a virgin.

"I think this calls for a celebration. I know you're not happy about the way things have gone, but we should try and make the best of it, don't you think?" Jordan soothed her as he opened the door and led her into his little house.

She looked at the pine-plank table and gasped. Her trunk had been set to one side of the room, and her rocking chair had been placed beside the chair that Jordan would sit in when he was home. The light gleamed against the oiled wood. It was a silent message to her from Juanita. This was her home now, this was where she belonged, not back in the small room on the other side of the bar.

Jordan took her silence as acquiescence to the idea of celebrating. He produced two beautifully wrought crystal glasses. He filled the goblets with the best wine, and the wonderful scent of grapes and sunshine filled the room.

"To a long and profitable marriage for both of us," Jordan said, and clinked his glass against hers for the toast.

Chalcie sipped the wine numbly. His voice came back to haunt her. "I'll sort it out and divide the holdings later...." Wasn't that what he'd said? Taking it all away from her, not even leaving her pride unbroken.

Now, she had to say something now.

"Don't get your hopes up about the marriage being anything more than a convenience, Jordan," Chalcie said.

Jordan looked at her, his eyes narrowed.

"And what does that mean, Chalcie?" He looked devastatingly handsome in his dark coat and brilliantly white shirt. It set off his dark eyes, eyes that had a look in them that made Chalcie uncomfortable.

She fidgeted under his steady gaze. It was now or never.

"You'd better not be thinking of sharing my bed," Chalcie said firmly. She crossed her fingers, hoping that she had the fortitude to carry out her plan.

Jordan stared at her. Not a muscle on his face twitched, and his gaze never wavered.

"And why is that, *wife?*" he said softly.

Chalcie had never known that a soft voice could sound so menacing. She took a deep breath to steady herself. She had courage enough to carry this off. She had to have, or she'd have lost everything, including her virginity, to a cruel joke of fate and her father's will.

"I have no intention of sleeping with you."

"And why not?" Jordan's voice trailed off as he saw the set of Chalcie's chin. *Stubborn* was the only word for it. He had a sinking feeling that the sweetness of the kiss had been a lie, after all. She had no intention of treating him as anything other than a convenience.

How stupid of him, he berated himself silently. He had hoped against hope that Chalcie would actually see that he had some affection for her. He wasn't after her money, he had simply been trying to help her out and, in turn, perhaps gain another chance to press his suit for her affections. As her husband, he should have had at least a chance to win her over.

"Where are my books?"

"In the bedroom."

Chalcie stood up and so did Jordan.

"I can go in the bedroom by myself, you know," Chalcie said tightly.

"No, you can't. I'll not have you sneaking out the window and taking off into the night. I've had enough trouble with you to last me a couple of centuries," Jordan answered.

Chalcie walked toward the bedroom, her spine straight with anger. He didn't trust her. The bloody fool thought she'd run away from him. As if she'd do that. She didn't acknowledge that the thought had most certainly crossed her mind.

She marched into the room and saw the books laid out on the desk. She grabbed the book Dr. Guillaine had given her two years ago. She and her father had come down with fevers while they were crawling across the Central American jungles, trying to get to the Pacific and a ship headed for California. Her father had been vomiting what looked like black coffee grounds and was burning with fever when she found Dr. Guillaine.

The presence of the French physician in the rude muddy village had saved Kent's life. Once the crisis had passed, Chalcie had begun to pester the doctor with questions about medicine, about what would work as a febrifuge and as an emetic, which plants were deadly and which could cure fevers. She had suddenly realized that she needed to know everything she could learn about medicine. If the rumors she had heard were true, she was going to a place where they would be fifty or a hundred miles from the nearest settlement and doctor.

Guillaine, impressed with her interest, had given her one of his precious medical books to take with her. A compendium of cures and treatments, it had stood her in good stead innumerable times in the last year and a half. It was about to help her out of a tight situation yet again.

Flipping open the book, she pointed to the index.

"There, that's why you're not about to touch me," she said.

Jordan took the book, frowning.

"What has this to do with me?"

"Look at it, you fool." Chalcie's temper was beginning to boil.

Jordan took a deep breath and his jaw tightened as he tried to restrain his anger.

"May I suggest that you don't address me like that again?" Jordan said quietly. "I detest physical violence, particularly toward a woman, but if you persist in being a bitch, I'm going to turn you over my knee and take steps to curb that tongue of yours. I don't like being called a fool, especially by my wife." He stated the request mildly, but there was an underpinning of steel in the words.

Jordan turned back to the book and began to reread the index, frowning in puzzlement. He had no idea where this woman had managed to put her hands on such a book, but she should have been ashamed of herself to acknowledge that she had seen the words in it, much less understood any of it.

Medical indeed… Jordan could feel his cheeks growing red with embarrassment at what was contained in the pages.

He continued to read the list, and his frown of puzzlement grew deeper.

"What is this supposed to mean?"

Chalcie removed the book from his hands and closed it gently.

"If you noticed, almost three-quarters of the book was devoted to the discussion of various venereal diseases and how to control and cure them. Now, the cures are still under discussion, but the diseases are not. And here you are, a fine muscled specimen of a man, with whores ready to soothe your every ache, as I'm sure they've done in the past." Chalcie's voice almost dripped with venom.

"And?" Jordan didn't like the direction the discussion was headed. He'd expected to have her warming his bed by now.

"And I have no intention of allowing you to infect me. I'm not going to die of a venereal disease or be rendered sterile so I cannot have children because you've been infected while having your fun with those women in your bawdy houses."

Jordan looked at her in amazement.

"Well, I'll be damned. You think I'm infected?"

Chalcie nodded smugly. She ignored the thundercloud darkening his face.

Jordan had never been so insulted in his life. She mistrusted him that much to think that he'd come to her bed with the pox? He was offended to the very depths of his being. He knew women, true, but they were clean and wholesome women, not the poxed ones who ran at the edges of the town. He'd never had so much as a complaint to take to the doctor. If he hadn't been a gentleman, he would have instructed her on the spot about how a woman checked a man for diseases. He knew enough about the whore's trade to know how they checked for such things.

And she sure as hell hadn't been too worried about that in the morning when she lay in the fur blanket and rubbed herself against his manhood. No, she hadn't been objecting then to fulfilling a woman's role in the marriage bed!

"I'm not willing to find out. You'll not come to my bed until you can prove that you're free from infection." Chalcie smiled triumphantly. She had him now. She was in charge again.

God, don't tempt me, Jordan thought silently. Given any encouragement at all, he would have loosened his britches and showed her exactly what to look for and where, and prove to her once and for all that he was clean. He was so angry that he had to get away from her before he did something no gentleman ever did with a lady. Prove it indeed! Did she know what she was asking, or had all that description in the medical book been only so many words to her?

Jordan stalked over to the window and looked out at the deep velvet night. In the distance he could hear the miners still shouting and carrying on about the marriage. Little did they know what hand fate had dealt him tonight.

"Chalcie, have you ever thought that maybe you don't want to make love to me because you're afraid that you can't please a man?" he asked softly.

He heard Chalcie's gasp, and if there had been any way to call back the cruel words, he would have.

"What do you mean, I can't make love?"

"I mean that maybe your father was right. He said that he wanted for you to be married, because you needed to learn to be a wife and mother. He saw that you were the consummate businessman, better than anyone in Sonora, he said. But you are tough. You've learned to defeat any weaknesses, and in doing so, you've stopped being a woman. And he was wondering if you were capable of being a wife and mother and of being in love."

"I am capable," Chalcie said, stung by the criticism.

Jordan shook his head slowly. "Not from what I've seen," he said. "It's gold and land that bring out the passion in you, not love."

Jordan's voice was taunting her. He had hit at a weak spot. A worry that had come back to haunt her now and again when she looked at men and saw only competitors, never suitors or lovers.

But it was different with Jordan. She had felt the heat

between them. She had known that he wanted her and she wanted him. She had even offered herself to him earlier, and all he had done was turn her down.

"I can love if I want to."

"Prove it. You concentrate on business because you don't have any of the womanly feelings left anymore. They've been lost along the way and you'll never try to find them again on your own. Oh, your father did a good job on you, leaving you a wonderful, creative business-woman who hasn't any understanding at all of love," Jordan accused.

"No...!" Her voice trailed off into a hiccuping cry.

He was dashing her hopes. Did he really believe what he was saying? Oh God, what if it was true...?

It was a marriage that was doomed. Better if she had left everything and gone off to Murphys or Boston and buried herself in the life of a spinster. She wanted to run from the house and keep running until she had buried herself in the ice and snow and let the numbness take her.

Why had Jordan rescued her? Why hadn't he allowed her to die on that mountainside? That would have been the more compassionate way to deal with her. Then she wouldn't have to live with the absolute knowledge that she was worth nothing by herself, that the only reason Jordan had married her was for the Kent holdings. He didn't even think that she could love him, and what would a marriage be without love?

"Oh, God..." she whimpered again. All she wanted was the chance to be happy, and now it had been taken from her. Jordan had everything and she had nothing, not even the hope of love from her husband.

Jordan spun around and was shocked by the look on her face. Her eyes were wide, her mouth looked as if that sweet smile would never reappear, and traces of tears had begun to wash her face. Even the fierce red of her hair seemed wilted and subdued.

The ache between them was growing into a chasm that

would never be healed. They'd beaten each other with words until all the "I'm sorries" in the world wouldn't wash out the pain that they'd dealt each other.

"Chalcie, I'm sorry. I didn't mean that...." He reached out for her, trying to make amends. She'd hurt his pride, but nothing compared to what he'd done to her.

"Don't touch me," Chalcie said, her voice dead. "Not now, not ever. You don't want to have a wife like me. You'll have a chance later to have the kind of woman you want. But leave me alone."

"Chalcie, please. I said I was sorry. I apologize."

Chalcie straightened and stared at Jordan. He must never suspect that she had thought she might be in love with him. That all she had wanted was time to become used to the idea of being married. Jordan had hurt her far more deeply than he would ever realize. And she must never lie to herself again about being able to love.

"I'll be your wife in name, and I'll sleep here on the rug in the parlor, and you can pretend to your men friends that it really is a marriage. I'll even cook for you, damn your black heart. But I'll never grace your bed as long as you live. Go back to your whores, Jordan de Chatain, because I don't want you."

Chapter Twelve

Chalcie made a bed for herself in front of the fireplace. First the two blankets that had been on her own bed, and then the fur-lined one that had covered Jordan and her on the mountains. She unrolled the pelt and buried her face in the softness. The smell of snow and smoke still clung to the fur and another, almost indefinable scent that reminded her of Jordan.

Her heart contracted. This was not the marriage she had wanted for herself. Whatever chance she'd had of being happy in her marriage had been snatched from her, first by her father, then by Ames, and now again by Jordan's ambitions for her money.

"Damn and double damn," Chalcie swore. "I never should have given in and married. I should just have walked away."

"Chalcie?" Jordan was standing at the bedroom door. He had taken off his shirt and boots. He was clad only in his pants, and they were tight enough for her to see that there was at least one thing that Jordan wanted from her.

He looked magnificent. His body was beautiful, and the light dusting of black hair made her want to touch him, excite him, make him want her the same way that she wanted him. The firelight made him a study in shadow and light, and her eyes were inevitably drawn back to his tight black pants and the very clear outline of his manhood.

Chalcie looked up at him, and he moved swiftly toward her.

"Please don't cry. We've said terrible things to each other, but it isn't right for you to cry on your wedding night. Please, forgive me and come join me in our marriage bed." Jordan knelt beside her and rubbed a thumb over her cheek. "Give me time. I can teach you whatever it is that's been missing from your life. Just give me a chance."

Chalcie shook her head. She knew why Jordan had come to her. He wanted to make certain that she was truly his, so the money would be his, too. Didn't he understand yet? He didn't have to act like the loving husband. The Kent holdings were his now. He didn't have to try to secure his position by making love to her.

"Then you won't forgive me?" Jordan's voice was hollow.

Chalcie turned her face away from him.

"No, you won't. At least not yet." Jordan sighed. "Then I suppose the only thing I can do is give you the wedding present that has been lying on my bed for the past few hours and hope that eventually you will come to trust me enough to allow me to make you my real wife," Jordan said regretfully.

Chalcie stared up at him in surprise and confusion. Her wedding present? But how could he have found anything to give her when he'd only known a few hours ago that they would be married? And she had nothing for him! It pained her deepest, most proper Boston heart that she had nothing to give her new husband.

"Here. She's been waiting for you," Jordan said as he returned from the bedroom. He was carrying a small orange-and-white ball of fur. Two golden eyes opened and stared at Chalcie as Jordan carried the cat toward her.

"Oh, Jordan…" Chalcie was truly touched. He was giving her his cat, the one that looked so much like Ginger.

She felt the tears start to roll down her face again as she reached up and took the unresisting kitten into her arms. The cat never stopped purring.

"I had hoped that we would share her. She could be the beginning of a real family for us. Then later we'd have the children and kittens and..." Jordan stopped suddenly. He was saying more than he'd ever intended. He had never told anyone about his dreams for his own life as he grew older. There wasn't a man he knew well enough to tell his wishes and dreams to. He sometimes thought that of all the men in the gold country, he was the only one who sometimes hurt from wanting a settled home and family. He had lied when he told Chalcie that it didn't bother him to leave the farm back in Texas. He hadn't wanted the land, but he'd wanted the family. Even then, there was no special woman, no special place for him, so he'd moved on, looking for his dreams. The money had come easily, the family had not. He had built his home in Sonora, knowing that this was the last place he would run to. He would find his wife and his family here and be content with what California offered him. And now, by a strange quirk of fate, he was tied to a woman who might never be the wife and companion that he craved.

Chalcie blushed and then hugged the cat closer. He was talking about children as if he thought she'd be able to become something more than a person who saw only gold and land as the reason for living. Could he really feel that way?

"No, not yet..." she whispered. She didn't trust him yet. In time, perhaps, but right now she hadn't healed from the words that had been spoken. Now they could share the cat, and perhaps in time they would come to trust each other, and then they would share other things, too.

"Thank you," Chalcie said. "I wish I had something to give you that was as precious."

Chalcie didn't see Jordan open his mouth and then close it. If she didn't see that giving him her love would mean infinitely more to him, then she would have to discover it on her own. He wasn't going to give her any hints.

"If you change your mind about sleeping with me, I wouldn't mind a bit," Jordan said pointedly.

Chalcie didn't lift her eyes from the cat. She wanted to go with Jordan. God, how she wanted to sleep with him on her wedding night. But not until she could trust him. Not until she knew that he loved her and not her money.

"I can't, Jordan. Not now." She said it softly, but he still heard every word loud and clear.

Chalcie lay awake for hours, aching with desires that raged within her. She wanted to get up and go into that bed and be with her husband. She wanted to make love to him, to kiss him everywhere she could reach, to touch him and explore places she had never investigated before on his body. She wanted all of it and knew that once she had it she would be fulfilled. But she didn't dare go to him. He had said she didn't know how to love. She was terrified of finding out that he was right.

Instead, she snuggled with the cat and finally, in the early morning hours, managed to drift off into a nightmare-filled sleep.

By the time she awoke, Jordan's bed was empty and cold. She had promised herself that she would only look in the room, then straighten what needed to be straightened. Instead she lay on the bed and closed her eyes, fantasizing about the man who had slept there. Jordan found her there when he returned home, still asleep, with a smile on her lips.

It's a start, he thought wryly. At least he had a chance.

It took Chalcedony days to recover from her ordeal on the mountain. She huddled in front of the fire in the main room and stared at the leaping flames. She managed to prepare meals for Jordan but was barely able to choke down enough to sustain herself. Chalcie and Jordan talked, but their conversation was stilted and formal, not at all what they really wanted to say to each other.

Chalcie longed to tell Jordan that she kept seeing the faces of the men she had killed, and everything she cooked had the taste of wild onions and the dark bitter mushrooms. If she could have confided in him, it might have eased some of the pain and confusion that she felt. She wanted to tell him that she would like a chance to make the marriage work, but every time she thought about talking with Jordan, her well-developed sense of self-preservation took over. She had spent long years learning not to trust men, and it wasn't going to be possible to change that training over-night.

Jordan wanted to tell her that he hadn't even done an inventory of the Kent holdings. They were hers, he had decided. The only way he'd ever manage to make Chalcie trust him would be to convince her that he wasn't interested in her holdings.

Neither of them confided in the other.

Chalcie wept herself to sleep night after night. Jordan would come to the doorway and listen to her sobs and know that there wasn't any way that he could comfort her, at least not yet.

"Juanita, you've got to help me. It's been two weeks and I still haven't managed to get so much as a kiss from her. I'm not repulsive, am I?" Jordan cornered Juanita in the back of the bar during a slack time. He knew that Chalcie was her best friend, and he hoped that she could talk some sense into his wife.

"I'll see what I can do," Juanita promised. "I'll go visit her again this afternoon. I already visited before to tell her that no one was watching the books and that we needed to send down for supplies again, even if the roads are almost impassable. Damn that Houlihan anyway. I know the pack train came in, but no one seems to know what he did with

the goods that he brought. They've got to be around somewhere, but I can't find them."

"No use trying to send down for more supplies. No one
can get through right now. I'll share what I have on hand
at the Dry Gulch for both saloons."

Chalcie sat in the rocking chair, held the cat and brooded.
She stared out the window at the mines, gashes in the earth
that looked as painful as the ache in her heart. Juanita had
sent word that she'd be coming to the house again that
afternoon. The first time Juanita had come was to demand
some kind of direction for the C. K. Saloon and fandango
parlor. This time, she was almost sure, Juanita was going
to give her another lecture on being a good wife.

"So I'll let her lecture, and maybe she can give me a
hint on how I can make Jordan fall in love with me instead
of falling in love with my money...his money," Chalcie
hastily corrected herself.

She let Juanita in and hugged her friend. She hadn't realized until that very moment just how much she had
missed the daily banter with Juanita.

Juanita didn't waste any time getting to the heart of the
matter.

"Why aren't things going better between you and Jordan? He's out every night until all hours, and I see him
around town with those fancy ladies of his. That's not the
way it should be with a brand-new couple, Chalcie," Juanita said reprovingly. She wasn't really speaking the truth,
but maybe she could make Chalcie jealous enough to jolt
her out of this strange apathy.

"He didn't marry me with the intention of making me
either his bride or his business partner. He wanted the Kent
holdings and now he's got them," Chalcie said bitterly.
"Don't you think that if there was a chance of a romance,
I would know? But he doesn't even like me...." Chalcie's
voice wobbled with the last statement.

"The money, always the money. How do you know
that's all he wanted? Have you discussed this with him? Is

that something he said to you—'Chalcie, I don't want you interfering in the business and I don't intend to try and make this a real marriage'?'' Juanita waited for Chalcie's answer. She intended to confront her if she tried to lie about what Jordan had said to her.

"No, that isn't what he said," Chalcie admitted.

"Good. Since he hasn't said any of that, why are you pushing him away?"

"I'm not."

"Liar. If you weren't, he'd have bedded you by now, and that bundle of fur and blankets on the chest tells me that you're still sleeping on the floor."

"He doesn't want me. I know he doesn't."

"Is that a fact? Is this a conclusion that you arrived at before or after you accused him of being infected, for God's sake! It's a wonder he didn't throw you out of the house for saying such a thing. And then you sit there and cry as if he'd wounded you to the quick by ignoring you. Woman, he's going to ignore you until you apologize and start to act like a loving wife."

Juanita shook her head in exasperation. "Don't you know how lucky you are? You may not have control over the Kent holdings, but you're not out on your ass in the snow, hustling to try and stay alive. At least you have a man who could care for you. Jordan is a good man, the right man for you. He's already made it clear that you cannot control him, and that's more than your father ever did."

"I don't try and control men, I just try and control my own life. There's quite a difference," Chalcedony answered stubbornly.

"And a bolt of lightning is going to come down from the heavens and fry you to a crisp for that lie."

Chalcie glared at her friend. Juanita didn't know what she was talking about. He came home, ate what was on the table and went into his bedroom and office, closing the door behind him. He rustled papers and slammed books, so she knew he was in there, but they had a minimum of contact. He made no demands or advances toward her, nor showed any interest in her. It was like living in a state of siege.

Even though Juanita was her best friend, Chalcie couldn't bring herself to tell her about the hurtful things Jordan had said to her. More than anything, Chalcie was afraid that Juanita would say that Jordan was right.

She was glad, in a way, that he continued to ignore her. It saved her from her own treacherously changeable emotions. If he had softened and come to her, she might have ignored what he'd said about her shortcomings. She was desperate for a touch, a kind word, something that would tell her that she was an acceptable woman, a woman who was capable of responding to a man.

"Juanita, I need to know something...." Chalcie's voice faltered.

"Well?" Juanita stared at her. Chalcie had suddenly gone pale, and her eyes were dark with sadness. Maybe, Juanita thought, she was finally going to discover what was bothering Chalcie.

"What do the women in the fandango parlors do to make the men love them? I mean, is there a trick that I've never seen or learned because I've only been around my father all this time?"

"What do you mean?" Juanita was trying to understand, but sometimes she was convinced that Chalcie spoke Greek instead of English.

"I mean, I'd like to have a chance at a real marriage, and as long as Jordan can't see anything interesting about me, I'm not going to ever be a real wife."

Juanita looked Chalcie up and down and almost laughed. She was standing there, all curves and curls, and she thought that Jordan was only after her money? Lord, how many times did she have to tell this girl that Jordan was crazy about her? The whole town knew it, why didn't Chalcie?

"Don't be an idiot. Give him a chance and he'll love

you just fine. There isn't any other secret except trusting him not to hurt you and, in turn, being careful that you don't hurt his feelings, either,'' Juanita said briskly. ''And stop thinking so damned much about your money instead of your husband. If you're wondering whether he loves you or your money, give yourself a little credit for being beautiful. Show him that this enchanting creature who is his wife is interested in him. Greet Jordan with a kiss, and let him guide you from there. It's time, Chalcie, or you're going to lose him.''

''How can I lose him if I never had him?'' Chalcie asked bitterly. She appreciated Juanita's bracing words, but she didn't believe her friend.

''How will you ever know whether he loves you or not if you don't give him a chance?'' Juanita argued. She stood up and slapped her hand against her skirt. She wished there was some way to convince Chalcie that Jordan was basically an honorable and decent man, and that he could love her for herself instead of the Kent fortunes. But until Chalcie gave him a chance to prove his love, there was little Juanita could do to help the marriage, which was foundering before it even had a chance to set sail.

''Mark my words, Chalcie, he is in love with you now. But if you continue to distrust him, the love is going to fade and you'll never be able to regain it.''

Chalcie wasn't certain that she trusted Juanita's assessment of her trouble with Jordan, but she was willing to give her friend's advice a try.

Chalcie was ready to greet Jordan with a show of affection that evening. She had fixed her hair with a blue ribbon and had rolled up the blankets and put them behind the chest, hoping he would notice that they weren't in their accustomed place and read her intentions into that gesture.

Chalcie waited. She could hear the sounds of the camp but not the sounds of her husband returning. Gradually her hopes, which had bloomed like flowers in the snow, withered and faded. She had rejected him too often. He wasn't going to come home.

Finally, when she had nodded off and awakened with a start at least three times, she gave up and unrolled the blankets so she could sleep comfortably. Taffy, as Chalcie had named the cat, mewed and moved close to her.

"I'll try again tomorrow, and the next day, too," Chalcie said drowsily as she stroked the cat. "However long it takes, Taffy, I'm going to show Jordan that we can be happy together."

Neither Chalcie nor the cat awoke when Jordan finally came in after having walked through most of Sonora to cool down the passions that still raged through him. If Chalcie didn't begin to accept him as a husband, he swore he was going to burst from sheer frustration. He looked down at her and shook his head regretfully. He wouldn't force her, not yet.

Jordan's fondest hopes almost seemed to be coming true the next morning. Chalcie got up and cooked him a special breakfast.

It was a change for Chalcie, too. The first sign was that the apple pancakes she made for Jordan's breakfast didn't taste of wild onion, just flour and brown sugar and cinnamon. She even noticed that the snow outside was blowing mightily and handed Jordan his heavy rawhide hat before he walked out the door. He didn't acknowledge her gesture, but he looked at her thoughtfully before he slammed the door behind him.

"You could have said thank-you, you bastard," Chalcie yelled at the shut door when she judged he was far enough away from the house that he couldn't hear her.

"Thank you," Jordan answered promptly from outside on the porch.

Chalcie's face burned with mortification. She had been certain he'd left!

"Damn and double damn," she fumed as she cleaned up the kitchen, slamming the tin dishes into the tub and pouring boiling water over them. She washed the pan and hacked at the last of a hunk of beef that Jordan had brought the day before. With carrots and potatoes it would make a good stew. But she still couldn't stomach the idea of adding onions and mushrooms to the mix, no matter how good it would have tasted. As she cooked, she talked to herself.

Juanita was right. It was time to stop pitying herself. She had to get on with her life. She could give the marriage a chance, if Jordan cooperated. At least she could find out if she really was crippled by what had happened to her in the past ten years. She would know for certain if her father was right and she was incapable of love.

Incapable of love—the words rang like the knell of doom. If it was true, what would she do?

"The best I could hope for would be to help him with the businesses. At least then my talents wouldn't go to waste. Maybe that would be enough."

It wouldn't make up for her own dreams, which would be shattered. The times she had said that if she was lucky enough to find the right man, she'd have a better marriage than her father and mother. She'd be a good wife, she'd make her man happy. She'd even help him with his business and use the talents that she had to give him even higher profits.

She placed the stew at the back of the small stove, adding plenty of water to boil down into a rich gravy by evening, and finished cleaning the section of the room that served as a kitchen. It was still early, plenty of time to take a bath and wash her hair. An hour later she was clean and warm and bored to tears.

This was the life of a lady that her father had wished for her? She missed the hustle of the town, the sounds of the bar and the ebb and flow of the camp life. She missed Crazy Mac's drunken midnight bagpipe serenades when he felt homesickness and melancholy creeping over him. She even missed worrying about money and finding new ways to outwit Jordan.

She had to find something to keep herself occupied. Irresistibly, her mind turned to Jordan's papers.

Somewhere in that bedroom lay answers to all the questions she had ever asked about Jordan. His history, his background, everything that a wife should know about her husband. His real worth, his land holdings, even how much he spent on liquor should all be in there, in his papers. She knew she shouldn't be tempted, but one of her worst traits, her father had always told her, was her curiosity. Curiosity and boredom together were deadly.

"I won't do it," Chalcie said aloud, pushing away the idea of snooping. "I'll write a letter to my grandmother, instead. She ought to know that my father died and that I am still alive."

Chalcie took out paper and pen and began to put down the first words she had addressed to her grandparents in years. They might not want to hear from her, but at least she had to make the attempt. This time her father wasn't around to take the letter and rip it up, as he had during the first few years they had been on the road. He had told her that her grandparents didn't care about her and that they'd be glad she was gone. Leave them alone, they'll only hurt you, he'd said, and she had believed him. Lately, though, a great many things that her father had told her were coming into question.

"If it's true, I'll never write again. But I'd so like to know what happened to them after I left. And of course I'd like to know about my cats...." Chalcie sighed.

The letter was signed and sealed, ready to be sent back east with someone who would deliver it to the proper address for an ounce of gold paid in advance. Any answer would come by the same route, if her grandparents were still alive and still cared to answer a letter from her.

Writing the letter, however, did not completely exorcise the curiosity that she had about Jordan.

"It's perfectly legal now, isn't it?" she whispered, smiling for the first time in a long while. "A wife should know about her husband."

She advanced on the bedroom, hesitating just a moment before opening the door. She ignored the pricking of her conscience and the certainty that Juanita would tell her she was being a fool. She was going to do what he had accused her of doing months ago. She was going to snoop into his business affairs.

"Fool or not, I'm not going to give up without a fight," Chalcedony said. "It is my marriage, after all. And it stands to reason that the more I can discover about Jordan and his business, the more chance our marriage will have of surviving. If the only thing I'm good for is business, then at least we can be partners."

The paperwork for Jordan's various enterprises was in plain view on the pine-plank table that served as both drawers and desk. Wooden packing crates had been used to support both ends of the plank and his clothes were neatly folded in the crates. Any other woman would have been delighted to have such a man for a husband, Chalcie thought belligerently. It irritated her that she couldn't find fault with him even there. If he was so perfect, why didn't he love her?

She pulled up the stool and opened the first of the marbleized green ledgers. Within half an hour, she had a rough idea of what Jordan owned and owed in Sonora. He was better off than she had expected, but even with her cursory examination of the books, she was amazed at the mistakes and carelessness that he showed in the running of the various enterprises.

For instance, there was the Mountain Jack mine that he owned with that man Tourelle. At the first of the year, before Tourelle came on the scene, the mine had been producing high-grade ore at a good steady pace. Then, a month after Tourelle bought in, the production gradually began to drop. Couldn't Jordan tell that the mine was being raped by Tourelle, his supposed business partner? She wasn't sure how Tourelle managed it, but she was certain that a goodly number of the miners who worked for the Mountain Jack mine were high grading it. Hundreds of dollars a day were being lost as the men walked off with the ore stuffed in their pockets, in their shirts and the packs that they carried in and out of the pit. The mine was as rich as ever, but the men were consistently producing at least a hundred to two hundred pounds of high-grade ore a day less than they had a year before.

Chalcedony shook her head in wonder. Her own father had fallen into the same trap, working with men who were liars and cheats. One of his partners had murdered her father and forced her into a loveless marriage. And now, God help her, her own husband was saddled with a cheating partner. Tourelle was the same kind of slime that Ames had been.

She was busily planning how to get Jordan out of Tourelle's clutches before she realized that she had intended to use the information against Jordan, not for him!

"It's just that I can't stand to see bad management," she said, excusing herself, and turned back to the books, only to slam her palm down on the pages again in frustration.

How could any grown, sane man spend as much as he did to keep a saloon going? He had a captive audience, he didn't have to play to them the way he had. Lord, the cost on the mirror alone would have kept her in whiskey for two months. What an extravagance! If she was his partner, she'd make certain that those crazy impulses to spend were kept to a minimum.

Then there was the matter of a sudden drop in the supplies on hand. Almost as if half of everything had suddenly been stolen from him. Bad management again!

"This man needs me more than I ever knew. I could have wiped him out six months ago and he'd never have known what hit him!"

"You could have wiped me out? Why didn't you?"

Jordan's silky voice jarred her from the numbers that danced before her eyes.

"Jordan, I..." Chalcie tried to think of something to say. She was trapped!

Chapter Thirteen

"**I**'m waiting. And by the way, don't try and explain away the fact that you were snooping around the books to find out what you could about the operations. I wondered how long it would take you to get back into acting like the consummate businesswoman that you really are." His words were obviously not meant as a compliment.

Chalcie flinched, and Jordan was instantly sorry that he had spoken without thinking.

"You wanted to know why I didn't wipe you out?" Chalcie decided to tell him the truth. "Because I didn't know you were such an idiot. If I had read these books before now, you'd never have stood a chance against me."

"Good thing you didn't have access, then. Think of it, Chalcedony. You might have ended up married to a poor man. And by the way, if you try and take action against me now, you're damaging yourself as much as me. Like it or now, we are married."

"I wouldn't..." Chalcie choked out. She stopped. He was right. If she hurt him, she could eventually end up hurting herself.

"I was just reading, that's all. I was going to help..." She stopped, realizing how lame that would sound to Jordan. He had no reason to trust her. "It's just that you aren't making the most of what you've got. You need a good manager, just like my father did.''

Jordan closed his eyes and muttered something underneath his breath. Trust her? Accept help from the woman who had nearly bankrupted him by cutting the price of everything from whiskey to bread in her attempt to retaliate against her father and him? He knew what kind of help she would give him and he didn't need it!

He wished he could trust her, but she had never shown any sign that she forgave him for their enforced marriage. He had thought then that what had started as desperation on Chalcie's part would blossom into love. But he was starting to think that his accusation had been true—Chalcie had lost the ability to love. Dealing with her was like dealing with a nasty-tempered rattlesnake. Furthermore, he had no doubt that she could be just as deadly.

"But I was trying to help you with the businesses!" Chalcedony protested again. "You're being high graded and cheated at every turn, and you don't even know it."

She stopped abruptly. Damn it, she hadn't meant to tell him.

"What do you know about it? You've never set foot inside the places I run!" Jordan roared, stung that she had happened on what he had suspected for months.

"I can read books, and your operation isn't all that much different from my father's mines. There are ways to stop the losses, if you'd trust me. Except that I don't *know* your mine or your brothels or anything else."

Jordan slammed the bundle that he was carrying down on the bed and advanced on her. "There are going to be some changes around here!" he said, his voice deadly soft.

Chalcie leaned backward, her eyes wide. "What kind of changes?"

"Stand up," Jordan ordered, not even bothering to answer her.

"Stand up?" Chalcie asked faintly.

"Do it!" His voice was getting louder.

Chalcie almost tumbled over the stump as she hurried to comply.

Jordan grabbed her to keep her from falling, and then, before she knew what he was doing, he whipped the old woolen shawl off her shoulders.

"What are you doing...no, stop, you can't..." Chalcie beat at his hands as she felt the old pink calico beginning to rip under his determined assault.

"I can and I will. You are my wife, after all," Jordan said, his teeth clenched. He'd had enough from this woman. He didn't even know why he had bothered to buy these damn dresses. All he remembered was that he had wanted her to look beautiful, like the other women of the town. He had wanted her to show off her fine figure and glorious hair and enjoy being a woman. It had been altogether too long since she'd looked as beautiful as she had that night when she came to offer herself to him, and he wanted that vision back. The pink calico dress had to go.

The cotton finally ripped and the dress parted down the front, leaving the sleeves hanging from Chalcie's arms while the bodice gaped, showing her pretty chemise and underskirt, which she was wearing for warmth beneath the old cotton dress.

"Ah, at last!" Jordan crowed. He grabbed the skirt of the dress and ripped it away, leaving Chalcie standing in her underclothing in front of him.

"What are you going to do?" Chalcie asked, her voice quaking with fear.

Jordan leaned down and scooped up the remains of the dress. He strode out of the room, and Chalcie followed him to the bedroom door and stared in amazement as he threw the calico into the fire and watched in satisfaction as it was eaten by the flames.

"What?" She couldn't even think of a way to ask him what the hell he was doing with her dress.

"Never, ever, as long as you are my wife, do I want to

see you wearing that hideous shade of pink again,'' Jordan announced.

Chalcie began to smile. ''Then what exactly do you expect me to wear? You've burned my one work dress, and all I have left is a fine velvet that won't suit for the rain and mud and snow here.'' He might be reduced to watching her parade around in her chemise and underskirt if he wasn't careful. And she hoped that if that was the case, her ''natural charms'' would work through his defenses that much faster. He couldn't be totally immune to her, could he?

''There are dresses on the bed. Navy and dark red woolens for everyday work and going into town. One fine cream cashmere that will finally show everyone what a beauty you are...the same color of the dress that you made when you came to me that night...'' Jordan stopped for a moment, still thinking of the way she'd looked and what a fool he'd been not to sweep her off her feet and tell her he'd marry her right then. God, she'd looked beautiful! ''And another two skirts and coats so that you'll never be cold again. Do you think I haven't seen the way you've huddled up to the fire with that damned pink dress and the old shawl? My wife should never have to endure that kind of hardship. Your father might have treated you that way, but I will not!''

Chalcie simply couldn't think of a thing to say.

''I hope you like them. I had them made up by one of the women. Juanita knew what size you were....'' Jordan was beginning to run out of steam. Suddenly ripping her dress off and burning it didn't seem like such a good idea now that he'd had time to think about it. What if she cherished that damned pink mess she'd been wearing? She'd never forgive him for burning it.

Chalcie saw the look on his face and almost laughed. He'd given her two wonderful gifts. First, of course, were the clothes, but second, and far more precious, was the knowledge that at least he was noticing her and what she was wearing. And she couldn't think of a better end for that damned dress.

"I'll go change right now."

"And put on your shoes. We're going out," Jordan said, relaxing once he saw the smile on Chalcie's face. He'd done something right!

"Why?" Chalcie asked.

"Because I said so, and because if you don't have those shoes on in two minutes, I'll drag you out of here without them. And by the way, it's cold out. I suggest that you wear one of the warmer dresses and the cape that's at the bottom of the packet. It should keep you warm. We'll be out for a while."

Chalcie started to object and then looked closely at Jordan. He could and he would.

Jordan nodded at the dawning comprehension on Chalcedony's face. He walked over to the stove and poured himself a cup of strong black coffee, watching as she scurried around trying to put on her shoes and fix her hair so she was presentable to the outside world. He smiled inwardly. At least she was taking him seriously.

A small thrill of pleasure shot through him unexpectedly as Chalcie stepped out of the bedroom. She had brushed her hair, tying it back with a red ribbon, and had chosen the dark blue woolen dress that had been sewn with an extra full skirt and a touch of embroidery from Juanita herself around the neckline. She looked beautiful.

Chalcie pirouetted in front of him, showing off the dress. She had never had anything half so fine since her father had stolen her. The new things almost made up for what she had lost during that crossing of the isthmus with her father. And to think they had been given to her by her husband.

"Thank you, it's wonderful," Chalcie said, and without thinking, she rushed over to Jordan and kissed him full on the mouth. She tasted the coffee on his lips and felt the sudden awareness between them that had been hidden all these weeks.

"Not now," Jordan said softly, though he reached for her as if he wanted to pull her back into the circle of his arms. "We have work to do."

Chalcie's smile faded. *Work to do.* He didn't want her. Suddenly she felt foolish for having kissed him. Obviously he didn't want that kind of physical contact yet.

"Ready?" He put the coffee cup on the back of the stove beside the tin of stew.

Chalcedony nodded. "Would you like to tell me where we're going?"

"You were looking at my books, I figure it's about time you saw the real thing. We're going to look at the de Chatain holdings. Once we've made those rounds, we'll stop by the bar and you can get a report on the Kent business from Juanita."

Jordan ignored the look of confusion and the slight flicker of hope on Chalcie's face. He led her out of the house and onto the main path through the town.

"Hey, good to see you, Chalcie. We were wondering when we'd have the pleasure of your smile again. Married life agrees with you."

The comments rang out from all sides. For the miners the romance had all the trappings of a roaring good drama that could have been on the stage. Instead it was set in the middle of Sonora and peopled with players they knew. Many a sideways glance said volumes about what the men thought the two of them had been doing while Chalcie had stayed hidden.

Jordan surprised her by playing to the crowd. His arm around her waist felt warm and comfortable. His gallant help in negotiating the treacherously slippery path made her feel cosseted and warm. Given half a chance, she could even have believed that they cared for each other.

Almost instinctively, she withdrew from his grasp. She felt confused. She found herself longing for his love, but the very thought of depending on him for support and comfort frightened her.

Jordan felt her shrink away and cursed to himself. He had almost thought for a moment that she was warming to him. When he spoke again, he was all business.

"I'd take you out to the Mountain Jack mine that Tourelle and I own but the road's impassable. This last snow shut things down tight. We've left two men up there guarding the work that was under way, but it won't be open again until sometime in May."

Chalcedony nodded. Her own mine had shut down a week earlier, at the first snow. She didn't approve of the miners who stayed and worked until the last possible minute. The chances of dying from the cold or an accident by miserable conditions were too great to be risked.

"As you noticed, profits are down at the Mountain Jack but holding steady at the Hatcher. The man who partners the Mountain Jack with me wants to buy into the Hatcher. Guy by the name of Tourelle. Know anything about him?"

"Tourelle? Not a thing, except that he's robbing you blind," Chalcedony said.

Jordan smiled down at her, looking for all the world like someone who was actually interested in her and her opinions. "Once we're home, you can tell me what you've deduced about the way Tourelle operates. I'd like to know if we come up with the same answers."

"If you knew he was stealing, why did you promise to sell off some of the Kent holdings the night of the wedding?" Chalcie challenged him. She had never forgotten the whispered conversation.

"Sell off the Kent holdings?" Jordan was amazed. "I never said any such thing. I told him to wait until the wedding was over, and then we'd sit down and split the profits from the partnership, and I'd take control of my portion of the mines. I figured that being married was about all the partnership I wanted at the moment."

Jordan looked at her sideways, surprised at the shock on

her face. Had she really thought he was selling her down the river? No wonder she hadn't trusted him! A flicker of hope was being fanned into the beginnings of a bonfire. If he could make her realize that he wanted her as a wife and that he was willing to give her back everything that was hers, maybe then he could have a chance at fulfilling his own dreams of a family.

Five hours later, Chalcedony walked into her own bar, threw herself into one of the two good chairs and refused to move. She had seen more than she ever wanted to of the various de Chatain establishments in Sonora. She had also watched every woman in town make eyes toward her husband.

"Jordan, nice to have you back." "Jordan, will you be visiting tonight?" "We've got a game for you, Jordan...." It had made her boil with anger as the ladies strutted their all-too-obvious wares for him.

It hurt to know that she wasn't the only one to find him dangerously fascinating. She was bitterly aware that once again she had almost allowed a simple physical lust to cloud her senses. She couldn't let down her guard or she would give up everything to this man.

"That's it, Jordan, not another step, no matter what I haven't seen today," she announced tiredly.

"Good, because we're through. At least until the mines open up again," Jordan agreed. "Now, what do you think of what I've accumulated over the last year?"

Chalcie looked at him and then closed her eyes. She had a choice. Either she could make the first attempt to bring him into her life as an equal partner, or she could lie and try to use what she had found out today against him. If someone had asked her what her decision might have been fifteen days ago, she would have said she would use the information against him. Now, knowing that he trusted her, she wanted more than anything else to be a part of his life, both within the business and within the marriage.

"I think that we're equally matched. With the Kent land

and businesses, no one will ever be able to match your wealth,'' Chalcie said.

''I don't think you've understood, Chalcie, I don't want—''

Juanita interrupted him as she hurried up, her face in a worried frown.

''Jordan, we're running really low on the whiskey again—any chance that you've got some squirreled away in one of the storehouses?''

Chalcie almost choked when she heard the request. Why on earth should Jordan be supplying whiskey to the C.K.?

''Talk to one of my men. You know that anything I have I'll split with you. But we're getting damned low. It's worrying me. The men will do fine with whiskey and beans, but leave them without the whiskey to warm up and only beans to fill their stomachs and we could have a riot on our hands.''

Chalcie tried to interrupt and ask what the hell they were talking about, but neither of them was paying much attention to her.

Jordan continued. ''I'd give anything to find those supplies that Houlihan stashed. It'd see both of us through with no trouble at all. At the moment, I'm down to less than ten barrels of flour, and we've used up twenty from the stores. Same with the beans. It might even be that we have to close down the C.K. temporarily if we run out of stuff.''

Chalcie finally interrupted them. ''What the hell do you both mean? And what is this about closing down the C.K.?''

''Huh?'' Jordan finally paid attention to her.

''You heard me. What is this about whiskey and why would you close down the C.K.? Shouldn't you at least ask me whether I want the place shut down?''

Jordan looked at Juanita, and then suddenly it dawned on both of them. They had worked out their own way of dealing with the supplies shortage while Chalcie recovered from the kidnapping and the forced marriage. They hadn't thought to include her in any of their decisions.

"Ah, Chalcie, I think there's a few things we have to talk about," Jordan said uncomfortably.

"Oh, don't go sounding like you've got anything to apologize for," Juanita interrupted him. "All you did was step in and give us supplies when we needed them. Splitting things fifty-fifty down the middle, he's managed to keep both the C.K. and the Dry Gulch open from what he had on hand."

Chalcie's eyes were wide. So that was the reason all of the goods on hand listed in Jordan's books had suddenly been depleted. Jordan had been taking care of both bars. She was at once grateful and furious.

"Why didn't you tell me?" she demanded.

"Because you weren't in any condition to listen."

Chalcie couldn't argue with that. "But now we're running low on everything?"

"It's bad. And there isn't a chance in hell of getting another pack train through the roads right now. We're on our own until things open up again in the spring," Jordan said.

"So that means something will have to be shut down and it'll be the C.K. that goes, not the Dry Gulch?"

"Unless we find that stuff of yours. If we find it, we'll be able to keep everything open. It will be a mighty profitable year then. We won't be scraping the bottom like we are now.

"Chalcie, what do you think? We've only got enough supplies left for about a week. Do we close down the C.K. now or wait?"

"Why ask me? Do what you want, it's yours now anyway," Chalcie said bitterly.

"No, Chalcie, that isn't the way it is, and I'm not going to let you get the wrong ideas about what's going on. You're a part of this, so join in, all right?"

Chalcie stared at him, utterly shocked. Join in? He was treating her as if he wanted to listen to her ideas.

"Juanita, how about some tea for Chalcie and something a bit stronger for me. Then give Chalcie all the details about what's been going on with her property since our marriage," Jordan ordered. He wanted to make certain Chalcie knew that she was still the person in charge of the business. It had never been his intention to make her step aside so he could steal everything from her.

Juanita poured Chalcie a cup of the hot *manzanilla* tea that she kept on the back of the barrel stove. For Jordan she took out a bottle of the best brandy, straight from France, and poured him a generous libation.

"Mostly it's been a battle to keep things open. If it hadn't been for Jordan, C.K. would have closed down two weeks ago. Everything depends on finding those supplies," Juanita said, sighing. "We've looked everywhere for them but never managed to find them. It's getting worse. Even Eduardo is out searching for that hidden cache. It's costing a fortune to keep everything open. I think Jordan is right. Close down something until we've got more stock. Maybe the C.K. could reopen after the roads become passable again."

"And after you've repaid me one way or another, in cash or in trade. I prefer trade, of course!" Jordan leered at her, trying to make a joke. He already knew which way he'd prefer to be repaid. He just wasn't certain he could convince Chalcie that sharing his bed was a good idea.

"Don't worry, I'll make sure you don't lose any money on the deal," Chalcie said frostily.

Juanita looked inquiringly at Jordan, and he shrugged his shoulders.

"Let's go home and talk about that."

Leaving most of the brandy untouched, he helped Chalcie to her feet.

Chalcie ignored him all the way home, and Jordan was

seething with frustration by the time they closed the front door behind them.

"It's no use, Chalcie, I'm going to make you talk to me. There are things that have to be discussed."

Jordan settled himself in the log chair that had been carved from a huge stump and padded with old blankets.

"There is nothing to discuss. You have every right to do what you want with the C.K. and anything else that my father had. I'm not going to stop you."

"Is that what's bothering you?" He was ridiculously happy to know that she wasn't angry about his remark about paying him back for the supplies.

Chalcie nodded. "I thought that you'd want to take over my bar and everything else now, since you're already sharing supplies. It's only fair. My father did will it to you, you know."

"He did will it to me, but that doesn't mean I'm going to rip it away from you."

"Why not?"

"Because I don't need the bar or the land or anything else," Jordan burst out in frustration.

"Certainly you do. Wasn't it the Kent property that finally convinced you to marry me?"

Jordan wondered how she could be so mistaken. "No, it was not."

Chalcie narrowed her eyes and studied him. Maybe he was telling the truth, and then again, maybe he wasn't. Could he mean that he really thought she was attractive? Was he actually saying that she might mean something to him? Or was this just a way of telling her that not only didn't he want her land, which was unthinkable, but that he didn't want her as a wife, either. Was she losing him then before she'd ever had a chance to try and be a real wife to him?

An intense pain shot through her at the thought. Her hand went to her breast, covering her heart as if she could protect it when it was already wounded.

Jordan saw her wince and reached out involuntarily toward her, then withdrew his hand as she flinched. She didn't want to be touched, that much was obvious.

"I'll do what I'm best capable of. I'll help you with the businesses," Chalcie said stiffly. She was going to give up on this other silliness. She was good for business, not pleasure. She wasn't capable of either loving or being loved.

Jordan closed his eyes briefly. He had stood above her yesterday morning as she slept, staring at her. She had looked fragile and pink, beautiful and vulnerable. He would have given every ounce of his fortune to be able to slide into the rug beside her and make love to her.

"Chalcie, I want more than that from you...."

"I'll do what I can, Jordan. Give me time."

"And if it doesn't work? You're going to leave? You are that certain that the marriage will never work? Why? What have I ever done to make you feel that way? I told you that if you'd give me a chance we could make this work. Yet every time I try, something goes wrong. I'm sorry that I can't say the right things all the time, or that I can't read your mind and find out what it is that you want from me. Damn it, it's simple. I want a wife, a woman in my bed, a mother for my children. Can't you at least give me that?" Jordan stood up and began to pace the room angrily. She already wanted to make certain that she didn't walk away broke? He could end the farce of a marriage right here and now, give her everything back and be done with it.

"I don't know how!" Chalcie said softly, but Jordan didn't register the words. He was too wrapped up in his own frustration and anger at the situation. Moodily, without looking at her again, he left the house. There would be better company at the Dry Gulch.

He almost opened his mouth to tell her that she didn't even have to stay the night if this was what he got for being so damned eager to include her in his life. This was what he got when he decided that he'd give one last, valiant try at making the marriage succeed. She slapped him down again!

Jordan was ready to walk out and not come back. He'd done everything in his power to show her that he wanted to make her his wife. He'd damn near come right out and told her that he thought he was falling in love with her. He'd bought those dresses when he saw that she was cold. He'd promised to give her back every last bit of her inheritance. And she still couldn't even tell him that she loved him?

The hell with it.

Chapter Fourteen

Chalcie couldn't believe that Jordan had managed to elude her every wile for so long. Jordan hadn't even approached her with so much as a remark that could be considered suggestive. He was polite, kind, considerate, and he was driving her mad! Chalcie stared moodily into her cup of tea, wishing that she had learned to read leaves somewhere in her travels. Maybe the swirls in the bottom of the cup would have been more successful in guiding her life than she had been. She had the disquieting feeling that something was lurking in the future. She wished that she had an idea about whether it was something she would like or heartily dislike. Tea leaves would have been adequate, but finding a fortune-teller would have been even better.

She took another sip of tea and frowned. There was plenty to worry about. Tourelle was still robbing Jordan blind. They were literally scraping the bottom of every barrel they had. Food was running out. Weather or not, passable roads or not, they might still have to send down a pack train to bring in the bare essentials that would allow them to survive the winter.

At least the C.K. was still open. Jordan had been more than fair. When he'd realized how upset Chalcie was about the possibility of closing the bar, he'd tried to keep it running, even if the Dry Gulch suffered. Jordan had shared equally everything he had in storage for all the shops and bars, but it wasn't enough.

Jordan. Even the uncertainty of business wouldn't have been so terrible if her own body hadn't conspired against her. She could concentrate on the books for hours each day, but when Jordan came home, she was aware with every fiber in her being that he was a physically attractive male. In plain language, she lusted after him. Never, in all her years, had she desired a man as much as she desired Jordan. Her body ached with wanting him to touch her, but he never seemed to look at her.

She had tried to let him know that she was interested in him, but he seemed to be oblivious to the mounting tension. There were times when she considered attacking him, ripping the clothes off his body just as he had done to her, but for a different reason, and showing him exactly what she wanted. She'd never found the nerve to do it, though.

Her thoughts were interrupted as Juanita threw open the kitchen door and hurried in, bringing the smell of snow and a frigid blast of air with her.

"Close the door, quick," Chalcie ordered, shivering.

"Bother the door. My Eduardo's done something wonderful! It couldn't have happened at a better time. Come on, I've got something to show you," Juanita said. Her normally dusky cheeks glowed red from the cold, and her black eyes shone with delight.

"What did you find? An extra bottle of whiskey so that we don't have to take away from the Dry Gulch to keep the C.K. going?"

"Better than that! Grab a shawl and come with me. I want to show you the hidden treasure that's just been dug up."

Chalcie's mouth dropped open and then she whooped in delight. "Eduardo finally found the lost supplies—that's it, isn't it?" She hardly dared to hope. It would be such a blessed relief to be able to tell the miners that the rations had been found and the store could sell them whatever they needed.

"Come on and I'll show you!" Juanita hurried back out the door.

Chalcie hitched up her heavy woolen dress and followed Juanita out into the gloom. Struggling through snowdrifts and climbing over felled logs made it difficult to walk, but she didn't care. The sheer physical exercise woke her up, shaking off the worry about Jordan's true intentions to her. The deepening shadows of late afternoon darkened the hills almost to black, and the clouds creeping over the mountaintops promised even more snow for the night.

"He did indeed find it. Oh, Chalcie, we needed those supplies so much. You should have heard the men complaining the last few nights. Some of them were wanting biscuits and even candy, and of course there's none to be had. Fights are breaking out, tempers are short…. This will cause the greatest celebration here since your marriage…" Juanita stopped short. She hadn't meant to say that.

The marriage that had started with such high hopes had all but fizzled. The light had gone out of Chalcie's eyes and Jordan was prowling the town like a wounded bear, ready for a fight with anyone who wanted to risk it. Juanita almost wished that she had let Chalcie go to Murphys or Boston rather than endure the kind of pain that the marriage had produced.

She put the thought aside as they approached the mound of snow that was being excavated by two men from the bar.

"You can barely see the shack, the snow's so deep. We'd searched everywhere else, and finally Eduardo sat down and tried to retrace Houlihan's steps when he brought the supplies from Stockton. There wasn't too much time between bringing the mule train in and kidnapping you. Eduardo talked to several other men, and they remember that Houlihan had just walked through town and then to the stables and looked around. Toward the back there are a couple of sheds that no one knew anything about. He bashed a lock and opened the door and there it was, all the stuff you've been looking for!''

It was obvious that Juanita was almost bursting with pride for Eduardo's superior intellect. She gestured toward the dilapidated building with the tin can lantern that she carried.

"We knew that skunk Houlihan didn't have the brains or the time to hide several thousand dollars' worth of food before he and Ames came after you. They would have been too busy trying to plan your father's murder, but it took Eduardo to figure it all out.''

Chalcie shivered at the words. So much had happened in the past few months, and most of it had been bad. About the only bit of good news concerned Eduardo and Juanita.

"When are you going to get married, Juanita? Eduardo is perfect for you.''

"Oh, no—no marriage. I wouldn't do that. Besides, I'm not in love,'' Juanita protested hastily, but Chalcie could see the blush that rose in her cheeks.

Juanita was anxious to change the subject. She picked up the shovel that leaned against the side of the shanty and scraped away the snow that had drifted in front of the haphazardly nailed slats that served as a door. She set the lantern down on a ledge inside the door and stepped aside so that Chalcie could see the bounty that had been recovered.

Chalcie stood in the flare of the light and looked around her. Her supplies…her flour and sugar and coffee and other comestibles. How things had changed since her father had sent Houlihan off to bring all this back from Stockton. If only she could turn time back! But then she wouldn't be married to Jordan—the thought made her heart ache.

She leaned over and lifted one of the bags that had been jumbled as they were thrown in the door to the room.

"Mice or rats got to the flour, but not so bad we can't use it,'' Chalcie observed, poking her fingers into the holes that had allowed the white flour to sift out onto the dirt floor. There was a scuttling noise and a brown tail vanished behind one of the sacks.

"Taffy'd have a great time in here, wouldn't she?"

"As if you'd let her out of the house long enough even to learn to mouse. You're spoiling that cat the same way you should be spoiling Jordan," Juanita said sharply.

"No I'm not. He has no complaints." Chalcie tried to shrug off Juanita's observations. She poked around the sacks and paper-wrapped chunks of dried meats.

Juanita shook her head sadly. No, things were not as they should have been in that marriage, but there was precious little that she could do about it.

"Raccoons have been at the lard and bacon. What they couldn't pry loose, they bit through," Chalcie said as she explored further.

"The whiskey is all right. There's no way the animals could get into the casks," Juanita said as she lifted the light higher so they could see to the back of the musty shed. A quick inventory showed that they had the tinned oysters she had requested, plenty of tinned peaches and oranges and sacks of dried beans, cornmeal and wheat. The sugar and salt were hard as rocks but could still be used for cooking once the teeth marks had been shaved off.

Chalcedony breathed a sigh of relief. They had been low on sugar for weeks, and the men's unvaried diet of whiskey and beans was wearing thin. At least now they'd have a few luxury items to sell to the men who hadn't spent all their gold on good times and wild women.

"Look, apples, crates of them. That'll carry the men through until we can find the greens to flesh out their diet," Juanita said. She pried up a loose slat and looked at the green and red fruits that were nestled in sawdust. She had been in Sonora almost twenty months and remembered with brutal clarity the ravages of a poor diet. More men had died from lack of fresh fruits and vegetables than in all the accidents of the year. In the spring they had been reduced to eating miner's lettuce and had been humbly grateful for the bitter bits of green.

Chalcie was already planning the feast for the evening. There should be a celebration in honor of the found supplies. Not only would she and Jordan eat well, so would the men in the mining town.

"Get some of the men over here and we'll start moving it all to the more secure sheds out back. And ask Hope to be ready to whip up some of her oyster cakes to be sold this evening. And for the men who can't afford that treat, I'll make cornmeal fritters. I need something to do this evening, anyway."

Chalcedony issued the orders as they closed the door and headed back down toward the store and saloon. "Someone will have to find Jordan and tell him to open the locks on the Dry Gulch's storage shack. He's going to be happy!"

"He'd be happier if you started treating him like a husband." Juanita insisted on turning the conversation back to the state of Chalcie's marriage.

"I don't want to talk about it," Chalcie said sharply. She was trying, for God's sake. Couldn't Juanita just leave it be?

Juanita stopped in the middle of the street, her hands on her hips. "Tell me, when was the last time you kissed him?"

"That isn't what I'm talking about."

"It's what I'm talking about!"

Chalcie blushed and fiddled with her dress. "If you must know, he hasn't so much as asked to hold my hand. About the only indication I've had that he thinks of me as a woman is the commission he gave to Lucy to make me new dresses, and I know you helped him with that. Otherwise he really doesn't notice me."

"And you wish he'd notice?"

Chalcie was silent.

"Yes, you definitely wish he'd notice." Juanita sighed as she watched Chalcie trying to form an answer. "Well, so do I, Chalcedony, because you deserve a good marriage. But you're going to have to work at it, just like he is. Both of you are stubborn as jackasses…'' Her voice trailed off as she looked down the street and saw two men and a woman approaching.

Her hand tightened around the tin can that served as a candle holder. Of all the times for Jordan to show up, this was the worst one, especially with that woman. Another few minutes and she might have pried some information out of Chalcie on the real state of affairs in the marriage.

In the past few weeks she had given Jordan every chance to confide in her, and he had ignored all her attempts to draw him into a conversation. He hadn't been inclined to tell her anything since he first asked for her help. Every time she'd tried to pin him down on what was happening between him and his wife, he had shrugged off her questions.

"Oh, damn," she muttered, and looked around for a way, any way, off the main street.

Chalcie, however, had already seen her husband. The greeting died on her lips as she stared at Jordan and Willy Hillis, the barman, and the woman who was accompanying them both down the middle of the main street.

"Chalcie, Juanita, what a surprise! The news around town is that you've found the missing supplies. I didn't expect you to be out looking them over quite so soon."

Jordan didn't seem the least bit disturbed by the fact that another woman was hanging on to his arm as if she belonged there. "I guess you can tell me all about it when you get home, Chalcie. And I need to ask about several entries from the past week for the store."

He looked down at the woman by his side and smiled warmly at her. He patted her hand, which was firmly attached to his sleeve.

"Jane, this is my wife, Chalcedony, and Juanita, manager of the C. K. Saloon. I'm sure you both know Jane, she's been singing at the Nuggett Saloon. She wanted to talk to Willy and me about the possibility of changing over to my place.''

Jane smiled at Chalcie as her hand lazily inscribed circles on Jordan's coat sleeve. It was a particularly intimate gesture that was meant to challenge Chalcie. Jane was telling her as clearly as if the words had been spoken that she meant to make Jordan her own.

''I'm sure she'd fit right in at the saloon. She seems to be at home in that type of atmosphere.'' Chalcie smiled maliciously. That would put the hussy in her place. Chalcie knew what the woman's game was, and she wasn't playing. Besides, Jane should know that fancy ladies rarely became respected wives, and Jane definitely qualified as a fancy lady. Her bust was pushed up so far that she risked catching the grippe when she walked in the cold air, and her hair had seen more than one bottle of peroxide to bring it to that strawlike color.

''Thanks, Chalcie, we think Jane will fit right in at the Dry Gulch, too. She should start tonight,'' Willy said, grinning. He was clearly infatuated with the woman. ''We're going to give your place a run for your money.''

Jordan smiled at Chalcie and raised his hat as if they were no more than acquaintances. There was nothing in his demeanor to indicate that they were man and wife. He strolled on with Willy and Jane, leaving Chalcie gasping in anger.

''That two-faced, lying, hypocritical, nasty excuse for a man, I'll split him end from end if it's the last thing I ever do!'' Chalcie hissed. ''I'll tell you, she isn't thinking of the time she's going to spend singing to the men. That woman's got something else in her sights!'' She stormed away, swearing as she went.

''That trollop thinks she can get her claws into him, is that it? I've seen that look before. She should know better than to try and hook Jordan. He's not going to leave me...''

Chalcie faltered in midsentence as a horrible thought took away her breath. It wasn't possible, was it? She wanted Jordan to love her. She had done everything that she could think of to make him love her, and now he was walking around with another woman.

"Now you see what I've been trying to tell you," Juanita said quietly.

"Now I see what? That my husband has found someone new?" she asked bitterly, the pain raw in her voice. "He doesn't need me anymore. He's got the money. Isn't that what I've been telling you, ever since he married me? All he wanted was the Kent money, not the Kent wife."

"No, that isn't true. You can't mean that," Juanita said angrily. "Lady, you'd better let him know, one way or another, that you care for him, or he's going to find warmth and loving somewhere else. Look back down the street and you'll see that there's even a woman ready and waiting for him."

"I'll try one more time," Chalcie said.

But how? It seemed that every time they were together they just argued. Jordan was right. She didn't know how to be soft and tempting for a man. She was beginning to wonder whether she had actually seen that flash of desire in his eyes when they were together on the mountain. She had looked up at him when they were lying beneath the fur, skin to skin, and his obvious desire was poking her somewhere in the region of her belly button. Of course that had been on the mountain, and she had just been rescued. Maybe it hadn't been lust at all but merely a sympathetic reaction to her nearness. Maybe any woman would have caused that to happen.

The thought filled her with sadness. She did so want to be special to someone. She could talk to Jordan, maybe even ask him to tell her what he really felt for her. He might say that he fancied her. Her spirits lifted at the very thought.

"No," she said, and her voice carried all the pain she had ever felt when she thought of Jordan, the man who had been at once her enemy and her husband. She couldn't stand to have the hope form and then be crushed.

But if Juanita was right, if it were true that he might want her... Oh, if it were true, she might still have a chance to be a loving wife and mother. She had never thought she could long so for such ordinary things until all hope of them had been taken from her.

Juanita saw Chalcie softening and decided to strike again, to make her point.

"Chalcie, you'd better do something soon. Jordan has been seen around town with a different woman on his arm every night."

"Every night?" Chalcie blanched. So tonight wasn't an exception.

"The rumors are getting louder and uglier. Aren't you interested in fighting back?"

"Oh, indeed I am interested in fighting back. Now that I've seen what I'm up against, I even think I can win," Chalcie said as she parted company with Juanita.

Jordan didn't know what was going to hit him when he came home tonight, Chalcie thought grimly. Jordan had never seen her in full temper tantrum. It would be quite a shock, Chalcie thought. Never again was Jordan de Chatain going to go walking around town with another woman's hand on his arm! He was her husband, and she wasn't going to share him with anyone else until she knew for certain that he didn't want her as his wife.

Chapter Fifteen

Chalcie had worked herself up to a fine temper when Jordan finally made an appearance. She was sick and tired of trying to make him notice her and then being ignored. She wasn't going to settle for being only a business partner any longer. Either he'd take her as his wife or he was going to set her loose tonight!

"Don't you come through that door expecting me to have dinner ready for you, or anything else for that matter!" Chalcie had been lying in wait for Jordan. He opened the door and ducked fast as she threw the loaf of fresh bread at him. The bread flew past him and landed, steaming, in the snowbank outside the house.

"Hey, what did I do?" Jordan asked, throwing up his hands to fend off any further attacks.

Chalcie couldn't believe that he'd even find it necessary to ask what he'd done to her. "What did you do? You stood there, in front of everyone in Sonora, flaunting your fancy woman at me, and you ask me what you did?"

Jordan shook his head ruefully. "But it wasn't like that. Jane is going to be a singer at the Dry Gulch."

"I don't care what she's going to be. You had no right to look like you were courting her, with her hand on your arm and making a fuss over her. You should have had at least enough sense of propriety to come over to me and act like you knew me as something more than a casual acquaintance.''

Jordan had to fight the little smile he felt tugging at the corners of his mouth. Was it possible Chalcie could actually be a little jealous?

Chalcie stared at him. Her hands clenched into fists. She was going to wipe that grin off his face. So he thought it was funny, shaming her in front of all of Sonora. She could just imagine what the men were saying now as they drank their whiskey and talked about what was happening in the town. She could even mimic the censorious voices of the miners. ''Oh, yes, did you hear? Chalcie wasn't woman enough to hold Jordan. He's already got another woman warming his bed.'' Yes, she knew what they were saying, and Jordan had no right to smile about it, either.

Chalcie stared up at him, her hands balled at her sides. She would have loved to smack that smug look right off his face. She lifted her chin and stared at him.

''You know what you've done to me, don't you?''

Jordan looked at her uneasily. He'd known Chalcie was a spitfire, but this was going a little far. He really hadn't meant a thing when he'd let Jane take his arm. Jane was just the kind of woman who did things like that.

Suddenly, he truly felt the dawn of hope. Chalcie's reaction was so extreme. Maybe this was indeed the first tentative sign that she had come to care about him.

''Chalcie, I didn't mean to harm you,'' he said quietly.

Chalcie shook her head. She had to fight the temptation to pound on his chest, to make him hurt physically the same way she ached emotionally.

''Jordan, tell me, what do you think the men have said about the marriage between the two of us?''

Jordan was surprised by the question. He had thought this was between Chalcie and him and concerned no one else in town.

''Not much. Mostly the men have said that they were a little jealous that I managed to take the most eligible woman in town. They think you're beautiful, and somehow it doesn't seem fair to them that I managed to marry you when I'm already one of the richest men in town. They'd rather have had you choose one of the poor miners for your husband.'' He didn't add that with her rosy cheeks and her golden-red hair glinting in the firelight, she was easily the most beautiful woman in all of California, and he'd fight to the death anyone who challenged his right to have her as his wife.

''That's not what the men are saying, at least not where Juanita can hear them,'' Chalcie said bitterly.

''What's she heard?'' Jordan was genuinely startled.

''They want to know how long the farce is going to keep up. It's a matter of open speculation about how long this marriage will last.''

''What does it matter what the men around town think? It's not important, is it?''

There was real pain in Chalcie's voice. ''How could you, Jordan? How could you hold me up to ridicule like that?''

''But I didn't—'' Jordan started to say.

Chalcie waved away his explanation. ''Don't tell me that you didn't say anything. It's all out there on the street— 'Jordan and Chalcie don't even sleep in the same bed.' I don't dare show my face outside now, especially after tonight.''

''Tonight wasn't anything terrible, Chalcie, believe me! Jane doesn't mean anything.'' He stopped short of telling her that he had been glad when she saw him with Jane. Somehow, he didn't think that would help his own cause at the moment.

''Not terrible? You with another woman, and not even caring when you meet up with your wife? It's bad enough that the men in town know that I was kidnapped and in their minds, at least, raped. It's worse that they know I had to come to you and beg you to take me in marriage. But now they're all certain that the marriage isn't going to work, because you've got another woman and you're bedding her within two months of your marriage.'' Chalcie's voice was racked with misery, but she refused to cry in front of this man. He'd hurt her, but she wouldn't give him the satisfaction of letting him know just how deep the anguish went.

"Look what you did. You meet me on the street, and I'm nothing more than an acquaintance to you. You don't remove the woman's arm from your sleeve, you do not come over and take my hand. You do nothing that would indicate that we have anything but the most formal of relationships.

"But then, a formal relationship is all you really want, isn't it? Business and good home cooking!'' There, Chalcie had said it. He could deny it all he wanted, but the wishes and hopes that she'd been building up from the looks and the words that passed between them were nothing but lies.

He might think that he could shame her in this way and still have her around the house, but she was sick to death of having her father, Houlihan, Ames and now her own husband think that she was a commodity to be used and then discarded when it was convenient. She wanted to be loved for all of her—for her brain, for her smile, for her sense of humor, for her body. She was so tired of everyone from her father to Jordan deciding that she wasn't worth anything.

Maybe the only way to break the cycle was to go as far away from Sonora as possible. If she left Jordan and the mining camp behind she might be able to find a man who wanted her for herself.

"Chalcie, I don't want any kind of business partnership. I want a real marriage, just like everyone else. I tried to tell you that months ago, but somehow you never believed me,'' Jordan tried again.

"Don't lie, Mr. de Chatain. You've made it very clear what you want from this marriage. You want to use my business sense as if we were business partners so that you can become even more rich. But as for making me a real wife in any sense of the word, that's not part of the game, is it?'' she said bitterly. ''You said that I wasn't capable of loving, even my father said so. And it seems you were right. I guess that I have no idea what love is, but it has nothing to do with the way we are with each other.''

She wiped away one miserable tear.

''Good God, think of it!'' she cried. ''My own father thought I was so undesirable that he had to attach a fortune to my getting married. And now, even after I have a husband, I'm not good enough at being a woman to keep him.''

Chalcie grabbed her shawl from the nail by the kitchen door, and before Jordan could react, she had vanished into the fast-falling snow.

''The hell with you! I'd rather leave forever than spend another night on your damned cold floor!'' Her voice floated back to him, borne on the wind that whipped the snowflakes over her tracks.

''Chalcie, come back!'' Jordan shouted, but there was no answer.

Jordan collapsed onto the stump that served as a chair for the table and buried his head in his hands.

How had it gone so far wrong? Didn't she know that he loved her, that he wanted her?

''No, I guess she doesn't.''

The realization came slowly. He'd spent two months being kind and courteous and courting her from a distance, thinking she needed time to come to terms with being his wife. Instead, she'd misunderstood everything he'd done.

''I should have made love to her on the mountain, and then there'd be none of this idiotic sleeping on the floor. She'd have been warming my bed instead of holding on to a cat in the middle of the night.'' He slammed his hand down on the table. ''Not any more, Chalcie. You come back here, and we're sharing my bed!''

The four walls echoed with the empty threat. He could say it all he wanted now that she'd left him.

Chapter Sixteen

"I'll run away and he'll never find me again," Chalcie said as she strode away into the darkness. The tears that she finally allowed to wash down her face made steam rise from her cheeks, then froze to little flecks of white around her chin. She wiped angrily at the evidence of her weakness. A man wouldn't cry, would he? No, he'd decide what to do about the problems that were plaguing him, and then he'd take action to solve those problems. She could be just as strong as any man she'd ever known.

"I'll leave, that's the simplest and cleanest way around it," Chalcie said as she stomped toward the C. K. Saloon. She'd tell Juanita she was leaving and then she'd strike out on her own. She hated to try to survive in the winter, but there wasn't any help for it.

Chalcie made it to the three-walled room that had served as her retreat for so many months. She sat for a while in the darkness on the wooden bed that she had slept on for more than a year. It was cold and lonely. Not even the sounds of the bar fights and the laughter of the men lightened the atmosphere. She wouldn't miss it at all, she decided. She would go away, change her name, and no one need ever hear of her again.

She imagined for a moment starting again, where no one

knew about her father's will, about her marriage, and now about the failure of her marriage.

Instead of a vision of light and happiness, she was surprised to discover that the future looked lifeless and barren without Jordan. No one would know her, and she would be totally alone. Jordan and Juanita would be gone. She'd never know whether Juanita and Eduardo managed to become man and wife. Jordan would eventually marry someone else who would make him happy.

Chalcie bit back a sob. She didn't want him to marry someone else. She wanted him to love her.

Then, through the other sounds, she heard Jordan calling her. He walked right in front of her room, and she sank back into the shadows, praying that he wouldn't find her so soon. She wasn't ready to talk to him quite yet. His voice faded as he walked to the end of the building and then doubled back to go into the bar. Even through the sounds of the miners in the bar, she could hear his voice.

At least he was looking for her, she thought in satisfaction. If he'd stayed in the house and eaten his meal and sat in front of the fire, she'd never even have considered going back to him. But Jordan cared enough to go out on a foul night and search for her.

Maybe things weren't as black between them as she thought.

If she came home again...the thought cut into him so deeply that he groaned with the pain. She had to come back, didn't she? Where else could she go?

He knew where she could go. She could leave Sonora and trek cross-country. She could stay in the woods, and never be found, or she could go up to one of the miners' cabins and have shelter and what food she could carry with her or trap. She was capable of just walking away from everything that had been her father's, and leaving him behind. If she wanted, she could disappear so thoroughly that he would never find her. She had threatened to leave the night of their wedding. Now she actually had.

If she came back, things were going to be different. First, they'd be man and wife in and out of bed. Before the week was out, she was either going to be sharing his bed and be a proper wife, or he was going to have, the marriage annulled. He wasn't going to live like this any longer. He couldn't stand the pain.

In fact, that was what he had planned to have happen this evening. He had waited two months for an order from San Francisco to be filled and hadn't had any hope of seeing it until the spring thaw. The roads weren't completely impassable, and this morning a man had ridden in and delivered the small packet to him in return for two ounces of gold for his trouble.

Slowly Jordan extracted the small yellow packet that he had been guarding so carefully. He'd planned to give it to Chalcie after they ate dinner. He had meant to show her just how much he thought of the marriage, and of her, with the present.

Now she was gone, and he didn't know if she was coming back. He slipped the envelope back into his pocket. Sometime later he'd have a chance to give it to her.

Jordan clapped his hat back on his head and started out into the storm. He had to search for her. Maybe if he tried to explain again, she'd understand.

"And maybe if I just pick her up, take her home and bounce her on the bed, we'll have all our troubles ironed out!"

Jordan began his search in the C. K. Saloon, but Juanita shrugged and shook her head when he asked if she'd seen Chalcie in the past hour.

"We had a fight," Jordan explained simply.

"Haven't seen her, but you might look in her old room," Juanita suggested. "I'm using it for storage, but the wooden bed's still set up in case someone is willing to pay for a night out of the snow and rain."

Jordan took the candle and lifted the calico curtain, marveling how a room could have seemed so alive with Chalcie in it but so dead with her gone. He could tell the instant he stepped inside that she wasn't there, but he saw that several of the cans out of one case had been taken, and two cracker tins out of another container were gone. His heart suddenly ached with a pain so bad that he wondered if he was having an attack. Had Chalcie run away from him? He hoped against hope that Juanita had taken the goods for use in the bar. He'd hate to think that his first idea about Chalcie running away forever was right.

He went up and down the paths behind the various buildings in Sonora. There was no answer.

"Damn it, woman, you could freeze to death outside on a night like this. You have to come home. We can still work it out," he called into the wind. He was terrified that Chalcie was gone from his life. He'd made a complete circuit of the town and come back to the starting point behind the C.K. bar, and there hadn't been so much as a footstep that he could have followed to find her.

He had a terrible feeling in the pit of his stomach, as if someone had kicked him and then decided that reaching in and knotting up his muscles wasn't a bad idea, either. His heart still hurt and he felt like sitting down in the middle of the snow and bawling like a kid. And all because of Chalcie.

He beat his fists against the wood of one of the buildings.

"How the hell did I know it would end like this? I only wanted a real wife, not some shadowy business partner who just happened to live in the same house with me!" He was bewildered and angry.

Finally he gave up the search. Jordan walked slowly back to the house. He ate a solitary meal and washed his dish. As the dawn struggled through the steadily falling snow, he sat in the rocking chair and held Taffy, happy for the comfort that the small furry body gave him. Taffy didn't seem to care that her back was wet with a steady rain of tears.

Chalcie would have to come back. She'd never leave Taffy behind. She'd come back eventually.

Jordan pulled the tiny yellow paper sack out of his pocket again and looked at it sadly. He had had such plans for a fine romantic evening. He knew that she could have read all his love into the small present. It was meant to show her that the marriage was a good one, and that he wanted a chance to make her truly his wife. Instead, he still had the present, but he didn't have Chalcie.

Jordan dumped the cat off his lap and stood up. Chalcie wasn't coming back anytime soon, that much was obvious. He walked over to the table, bent like an old man with tiredness and despair. He took a piece of lead and slowly wrote the only message that he could think of on the yellow paper sack.

"To Chalcie, with my love. I'm sorry."

Jordan left the tiny paper bag in the middle of the table where she couldn't possibly miss it if she returned, then he walked back out the door and toward the Dry Gulch Saloon. It was time, he thought, for a warm bottle of whiskey and another trek through town looking for any sign of Chalcie.

Chalcie made her way to the shed and opened it up. There was barely room for her to walk inside. She shivered. It was colder inside than out, and she heard the scurrying of mice in the back.

"Go away, mice," she said. She was too tired and too mixed-up to contend with any kind of rodents. For the first time since she left the house, she sat down and thought about what she had considered giving up.

"Chalcie, please come home…" Jordan's voice startled her. It sounded as if he were right outside the shed, and if she hadn't known better, she would have sworn that he was standing there talking to her, certain that she was inside the shed and listening to him.

"Please…" he said, and his voice faded so she couldn't hear the rest of the words.

Chalcie listened intently, but only silence followed. She didn't have the courage to go back outside and see if it was really Jordan. Probably it had just been her imagination. But somehow, obscurely, she felt comforted. Perhaps it was a message. Perhaps there was still hope for her and Jordan.

She pulled several of the blankets down from where they had been stored before being taken to the shop, and made herself a bed. She was shivering with the cold as she moved around the shed. She lighted one candle lamp, certain that it wouldn't be seen from the outside, and she foraged for a tin of the chocolate wafers that she knew were hidden in the bottom of one of the cartons. She'd been saving them, hoping to find someone who would pay the outrageous price she'd have to demand for the luxuries.

"I deserve a few luxuries myself, now don't I?" Chalcie said as she opened the tin and ate the first of the rich, wonderfully flavored biscuits.

Halfway through the tin, she'd decided that she definitely wasn't going to leave town and start her life anew someplace else. "I've started over too many times. I'm not going to do it again unless there's no other answer to my problems," she said emphatically, glad to get that much of her life settled.

Three-fourths of the way through the tin, she'd decided that she was going to face Jordan down and make him talk about their marriage and what they could do about it to make it a real marriage. She was going to force him to acknowledge that she was desirable as a real wife instead of just a business partner. Jordan de Chatain was going to desire her if she had to parade around in front of him naked and wearing bells and cheap perfume.

By the time she had finished the tin of biscuits, she had a stomachache and had decided that Jordan didn't stand a chance once she started on him. And to make absolutely certain of that, she was going to wait until first light, and then she was going to go into Chinese Camp for something that would assure that she was successful in luring Jordan to her bed.

Once her errand was finished, she was going to go home, cook something wonderful, sleep the rest of the day, and then she was going to seduce him. This time he wasn't going to stand out in the snow telling her that he couldn't make love to her. They were married, and she wanted everything that a normal wife would want from her husband.

Chalcie was still asleep when the camp began to come to life. It was at a slower pace than the summer mornings. Some of the miners who had claims close enough to town were still working in the freezing weather. Most of the miners weren't so lucky, and they spent the winter trying to build houses that would stand up to the rains and wind and snow. Because of their efforts, Sonora had already begun to look more like a real town instead of the mass of shanties and tents that lined most of the valley.

It was the sound of hammers one block over that woke Chalcie. She moved and her stomach growled a protest and sent a stabbing pain just under her breastbone.

"As long as I live, I'm never going to eat another piece of chocolate," Chalcie muttered. Her mouth tasted foul, and she could only guess what she looked like. There wasn't time, though, to go home and fix herself up. Besides, she wasn't ready quite yet to face Jordan. She had one more errand to take care of, and then she could start her war against his defenses.

Chalcie braided her hair, straightened her new wool dress and pulled the shawl close around her before she opened the door of the shed.

She peered around cautiously, but there was no one in sight. The snow had stopped falling, but the day was still overcast and sullen.

Chalcie set out for Chinese Camp, picking her way even more carefully than usual, because even the rough soles of her camp boots slipped on the hidden rocks. Snow was

beautiful but treacherous. It was a toss-up which was worse
to live in, the eternal heat and dust of summer or the cold
and slippery wet of winter. Someday, she was certain, California would be pacified and citified and cleaned up, but
at the moment each season brought its own little adven-
tures. Chalcie could smell the camp from several blocks
away. As usual, the main component of the distinctive odor
was that of food, and even though her stomach was still in
open rebellion, she wished that she had the chance to taste
a few of the dishes that were being prepared for the lucky
miners. In some ways the Chinese were better able to adapt
to the harsh conditions of the mining camp, and the way
they cooked was one of them. She'd tasted some of the
fried lichen, something she hadn't even thought was edible,
that one of the Chinese had shared with her, and it had
been delectable. She couldn't think of even one white miner
who would have thought of cooking lichen, and as a result
they ended up eating the same beans and bread day after
day. Chalcie stopped for a moment, then proceeded down
the winding path.

She hadn't gone all the way to Johnny Tong's store the
last time she ventured into the camp. She hoped it would
be easy to find him.

"Johnny Tong's place?" she inquired of the first man
that she met, expecting him to ignore her or to shrug as if
he didn't know. She was pleasantly surprised when he nodded and pointed toward the next street.

"Last shop, edge of camp," he said in highly accented
English.

Chalcie thanked him and hurried down the street, ignoring the stares of the Chinese as she passed. The snow had
started to fall again and the shawl wasn't warm enough.
She walked as fast as she dared, even though the exotic
sights and smells of the camp tempted her to linger and
explore. She was too cold to enjoy anything new.

Johnny's building was one of the few real buildings in
the camp. Most of the structures were even more primitive

than the ones that made up Sonora. This building had three sides and she could see a plume of smoke coming out the top, showing her that Johnny had at least the comfort of heat in his business.

Chalcie stepped inside and was assailed by the strange and powerful scents of the shop. First she noticed that it was warmer inside than in the snow. Most of the places in Sonora only gave respite from the wind and rain or snow. They weren't made to hold in heat.

Johnny Tong's, however, was warmed by a series of small braziers set around the shop. On one of the heaters a huge pot of water simmered gently. Chalcie sniffed the scented air. She could identify ginger and licorice, and something else more subtly pungent than she had ever dreamed of before. There were two men in the store, and both of them turned to stare in surprise at the white woman. Then, without another word, they placed their purchases on the plank counter and left the shop, leaving Johnny Tong behind to wait on her.

Mr. Tong nodded in recognition, bowing slightly toward Chalcie.

"Now you visit my shop as I came to yours. I am honored," he said quietly. Mr. Tong picked up the simmering kettle of water and poured some tea into a cup. He handed it to Chalcie, who accepted gratefully.

"Something to warm you, so you do not chill."

"Thank you, this is wonderful!" Chalcie said as she wrapped her hands around the cup and sniffed the delicious aroma of flowers and the slightly bitter smell of black tea.

"It will be good for your stomachache, too," Mr. Tong said.

Chalcie looked at him in disbelief. How could he have known?

"Your face shows every sign of that pain. I merely observe," he said, answering her unspoken question.

Mr. Tong was silent for a moment, giving Chalcie a chance to look around and become accustomed to the

strangeness of a shop that most white people, male or female, would never have even seen. He knew that something
desperately important must have driven her to come to him.
He could wait until she felt that she could tell him what it
was.

"I don't know what to say," Chalcie said finally. She
didn't even know what to ask for now that she was actually
standing in front of Mr. Tong. What could she say—pardon
me, I need a potion to make my husband so interested in
me that he wants to bed me?

Chalcie wrinkled her nose. She didn't want to do this. It
had been a stupid idea. Mr. Tong couldn't help her. She
drained the cup of tea and made an abortive move toward
leaving, then stopped.

The truth was, she needed every bit of help she could
get, and the women back in the fandango parlors had told
her that Johnny was the best. They'd helped each other
before, and maybe he could make another miracle for her
now.

"I need a potion," Chalcie said, and to her horror her
voice broke right in the middle. She coughed and tried
again. "I need something to make my husband…" She
flamed scarlet and stopped in midsentence. There simply
wasn't any way that she was going to be able to explain
her need delicately.

"Ah—you want something to make him more of a man,
is that it?" Johnny Tong was smiling as if there were a
secret joke that he knew about and wasn't going to share
with Chalcie.

Chalcie nodded dumbly. Even if she got the wrong herbs,
she wasn't going to be any more explicit. She'd just have
to hope that whatever he gave her would work.

"Wait, please," Mr. Tong said. He turned to the wall of
small drawers behind him and began to open first one and
then the other. Some of the herbs and spices he sniffed and
rejected. Others he took just a pinch of and brought over
to the heavy mortar and pestle, where he proceeded to grind

them into powder. The aroma of something sweet and pungent rose from the marble container as he worked with the herbs.

Mr. Tong tasted a tiny pinch of the mix, frowned and added more powdered ginger and a touch of something that looked like crystallized flowers.

Finally he was satisfied, and he poured the mix into a piece of clean white tissue paper. He twirled the ends closed with one expert twist and tied it off with red yarn.

"Here, this will do. It may be used in tea or in food. However you use it, it will work." He smiled again and bowed.

Chalcie took out her purse and began to open the packet of gold that she carried for emergencies.

"No, no payment. We are friends. This I do for you and for Jordan," Mr. Tong said, waving the gold aside.

"Please let me pay," she insisted.

"No, no pay!" Mr. Tong said again.

"Then thank you, Mr. Tong," Chalcie said as she left the shop. Someday, she hoped, she'd be able to return the favor.

Behind her she heard a burst of Chinese as the other men reentered the shop that she had just left.

Chalcie made it almost back to the main street in Sonora before she bumped into Juanita.

"Chalcie, where the hell have you been? You've led Jordan on a merry chase, and he's going to be mad as hell when you walk in that door!"

"No, he won't," Chalcie said smugly.

"You didn't see him last night. He was certain that you'd left him forever. Letting a man suffer for a while is one thing, scaring him half to death is another. I'd never dare do that with my Eduardo—he wouldn't stand for it," Juanita scolded her friend.

Chalcie smiled. She'd noticed the slip of the tongue, even if Juanita hadn't. Her Eduardo, indeed.

"Wait and see," she said. "I think I have everything planned, and tonight should be very interesting!"

Chalcie turned away from the saloon and headed back toward her home. There was a lot of work to do before Jordan came back. She muttered a swift prayer that he hadn't slept late and stayed home. It would ruin all her plans if he had. Besides, she was still shaky enough that she needed more time to think and plan ahead for the confrontation. She knew that sometime during the kneading of the bread or scrubbing of the stove, she'd find the perfect way to lead him into her bed and everything would be resolved.

The house was lonely and quiet when she opened the door. Taffy yawned and then jumped down from the table where she had been resting. She was carrying something in her teeth, but Chalcie was too tired to hunt her down and see what the cat had stolen.

The fire was almost out, and she spent half an hour building it back up until the flames were hot enough to warm water and she could fix herself a bracing cup of tea. She needed something to help her wake up. Then she'd start cooking. The tea wasn't as good as the one that Johnny Tong had served, but she made do by adding a little more sugar than normal. If she came out of this all right, she'd have to go back to Tong's and buy a whole carton of tea to brew for Jordan.

Chalcie had planned out the whole menu for the night including a couple of stiff shots of whiskey or whatever else she needed to give her the courage to go through with her seduction. She shivered when she looked over in the corner where the blankets should have been. It had been swept clean, and she knew then that Jordan never intended for her to sleep on the floor again. She hoped that it meant he wanted her in his bed instead. But what if he meant he didn't even want her in the house?

"I won't think about that."

Chalcie pared the apples for sweet dumplings and thought about Jordan.

She looked for a moment at the green ledgers that she could see through the open door to the bedroom. She dismissed them from her mind. She wasn't thinking about business, she was thinking about making her marriage work. Right now she wanted to make Jordan realize that she was desirable, ready for love and interested in having him behave as a real husband should behave. It had taken a night alone for her to realize that no matter what her father had said, she was a complete woman. She knew what her own body and emotions were telling her. She was ready for her husband to love her with the same kind of passion that she loved him. It was time to make him realize that he had a wife at home and that she needed some attention!

As she worked, she cataloged his good points. He was handsome. Every woman in Sonora knew that. The black hair, the dark eyes and slow smile, the deep voice—it was a package that was hard to resist.

"And not too many women have resisted it, from Jane on down," Chalcie muttered. She didn't blame him exactly, but he'd have to stop his roaming ways once they'd worked out the finer points of this marriage. She wasn't about to have a husband out on the town while she stayed home and did the ledgers.

The thought of his kisses warmed her, and she let herself float in the exciting daydream of what would have happened if he hadn't turned away from her while they were on the mountain. She was brought back to reality with a thump when she pared part of her finger instead of the apple.

She dumped the fruit into the pan and slid it onto the stove. She stirred slowly as the mixture simmered until the apples were coated with a golden sauce. She opened the packet from Johnny Tong and sniffed again to make certain that whatever the white paper contained would meld with the flavor of the apples and make it truly an apple dumpling to remember. The exotic spices tickled her nose as she sniffed, and then, muttering a prayer, she dumped the whole thing into the apples. She crossed her fingers and prayed that Johnny Tong knew what he was doing.

Several minutes later, the heady perfume of the mixture filled the room. She took a small spoon and tasted the apples, and closed her eyes in sheer delight at the delicate, rich, wonderful taste. Even if the stuff didn't do its job, it had made the best-flavored apples she had ever had the pleasure of eating.

"Just a little more sugar," she said critically, dumping in a few more lumps and stirring. She sampled the apples again and nodded. "Just right."

For the main part of the meal, Chalcie constructed a fine meat pie, adding just a bit of the chili that she had saved from the bunch that Johnny Tong had purchased. If it could burn Jordan's mouth a little, maybe it would start a fire in other parts of his body. Johnny Tong wasn't the only person around who could try to work miracles with herbs.

She swayed against the edge of the table as she thought of what she was planning. She wanted Jordan so much that she could have burst with the need. By the time the apple dumplings were cooked and cooling, with a crust of sugar lacing the brown pastry, she was fairly itching to put her plan into action. She had spent almost all day working in the kitchen, preparing for his homecoming. She was tired and anxious and more than a little frightened. It was the first time she'd ever tried such a thing, and she couldn't help feeling more than a little like one of the tarts in the second-story fandango parlors.

If she did try to make a life with Jordan, how was she going to tell him that she wanted to change the relationship? There didn't seem to be any way other than admitting that she had made a mistake.

What if he turned her down? She didn't think she could take the humiliation of having him announce that he wasn't interested in making love to her. She scrubbed at the table, removing every trace of flour and more than a few pine splinters in the process as she fought with her heart's desire to trust and love Jordan and her fear of rejection.

She washed, using warmed water from the kettle, and brushed her hair until it shone like the fire itself. The mirror showed her that the cooking and cleaning had put a bloom in her cheeks. She needed no help from any artificial color. She smudged a bit of charcoal around her eyes to make them look dark and mysterious, as she had seen the Gypsies in Texas do. She dabbed vanilla every place she could think of, so that she smelled like a giant cookie. She donned the new dress that had been made by Suzette, and she was ready for him.

Chalcie waited. The hours stretched on, and she began to wonder nervously if Jordan would ever come back to the house. A horrible thought occurred to her. He didn't know she was back—what if he had gone out on the trail, looking for her? He could be in danger!

"Five more minutes and then I'm going looking for him," Chalcie decided. "I can't stand the suspense." She picked up a cloth and began polishing the table for the twentieth time.

Her hands were sweating, and she was certain that by now she'd rubbed her eyes so often that she'd smudged the charcoal and made herself look as if she'd been smacked by someone. The apple dumplings were getting cold, the meat pies were going to congeal, and she was near tears.

"Everything is going to be ruined before I even have a chance!" she wailed, just as Jordan opened the door and stepped into the kitchen.

Chapter Seventeen

Jordan looked at Chalcie, his face thundercloud dark with anger. His black hair was tousled and wet from the snow, and it was obvious that somewhere along the way he'd lost his hat. His coat was drenched, and even his boots were soaked. He shivered just once as he glowered at Chalcie.

"Where the hell have you been?" he asked. His teeth were clenched with anger as he stood and dripped on the floor.

"I came home this morning...." Chalcie said, faltering. She hadn't expected him to be angry. At least not this angry. She watched as another shiver rolled through him. The poor man was going to catch his death if he didn't strip and wrap himself in a blanket.

"Get out of those clothes right now. We'll talk about last night after you've been dried off and warmed through," she ordered him. "I'll bring in the tin tub from outside and get you into a hot bath."

Jordan just stared at her as if he hadn't heard a word that she said.

"You stayed out all night, God knows where, and then you come prancing back into this house and expect me to just forget that anything happened? It doesn't work that way, Chalcie." He sneezed once. "You put me through hell last night and most of today!"

Chalcie nodded. "I know, and I'm sorry. But please, go strip out of those clothes. I promise you, I won't run away again. You can yell at me—or whatever else it is you want to do—after you're warm and dry, all right?"

She opened the door to reach for the tub, but Jordan grabbed her around the waist and pulled her back inside.

"I don't give a damn about the cold, and I don't care if I do catch the grippe. There are things that have to be worked out between us, Chalcie. I'm not ever going to spend another night like last night."

Jordan gave her one last withering look and clumped off to the bedroom.

Chalcie sighed in relief. She sprang into action, filling the pans to heat the water for the bath.

Poor Jordan. And she thought she had spent a bad night out in the shed. From the looks of Jordan, he'd slogged his way through streams and snow to find her. She was sorry for him, but it also gave her a warm glow to know that he'd cared enough about her to search all night.

Chalcie stepped outside to get the huge washtub and bring it in. She set the heavy tin tub down on the floor and began to fill it with steaming water. She was careful to mix just the right amount of cool and warm so he neither over-heated nor chilled again.

She wished that she'd saved a few of the herbs from the packet Johnny Tong had given her to put in the bath, but she wasn't certain that external application would have done as well as having him eat the potion. She heard his heavy wet coat hit the floor with a soggy thump. Next, another two bangs as he let his boots drop, and finally the unmistakable jingle of the pants and shirt with the metal buttons.

She heard him walking in the bedroom and looked up just in time to see him appear in the doorway, stark naked. Chalcie's eyes widened, and she backed up one step.

Jordan stood in the doorway for a moment and stared levelly at her, daring her to say anything.

"Oh my..." Chalcie said faintly. It was the best she could do under the circumstances. He was magnificent. No wonder women like Jane swooned after him.

"I intend to be able to walk around my own house dressed or undressed as the fancy strikes me and without any interference from you. We are married now, and I think you need to give a little more thought to my own wishes rather than your prudish sensibilities. I'm tired of bowing to what you want, do you understand that?" Jordan challenged her to say anything at all about his appearance. In truth, he was terrified that she'd turn around and run for the door, and he'd lose precious time getting dressed again. But he had to do something to shock her into seeing him as a man and a husband instead of an enemy.

He began to smile as he looked at Chalcie's face and realized that she definitely didn't see him as an enemy any longer. Her eyes were riveted somewhere between his belly button and his thighs.

"I understand," she managed to choke out. She gestured helplessly at the steaming washtub. She tried to talk, but nothing would come out. She was too interested in what she was seeing to be able to coordinate her vocal chords and make sense of what she needed to communicate to Jordan. Finally, however, she managed to tell him that the bath was ready and afterward they could eat dinner.

She watched in fascination as he walked over to the tub and slid down into the water. When he walked, every part of him swayed. She'd never seen a man naked long enough before to know that every part moved. Her fingers itched to reach out and touch him and explore, tweak and taste what had been forbidden for so long. She almost cried when the water covered the most interesting exhibition she'd seen in a long time.

"Stop staring and help me with my back, will you? There's no way I can twist my arms around to clean it," Jordan said. His voice was a soft purr, deep and throaty as a lion's.

Chalcie smiled. She moved closer to him and picked up the old rag and the piece of soap that she had placed on the floor beside the tub. This might be her first chance to actually seduce him. She wasn't sure just how a woman went about making certain a man was interested in her, but she intended to give it her most careful attention. First, she knew, she'd have to get close enough to him to touch him. When they were touching each other on the mountain, he certainly had exhibited every sign of being more than a little interested in her. She needed to make him have that same kind of reaction now, so her plan could work.

Chalcie moved closer to the tub. "Actually, if you want, I'll wash you all over. After all, we are man and wife, aren't we?" she asked sweetly.

Jordan turned and stared at her, and she almost burst out laughing at the look of absolute shock on his face.

"You aren't going to panic because I said that I'd help you, are you?" Chalcie dipped the towel into the water and slowly began to rub the piece of soap over the cloth, making a thick lather.

He watched her movements with fascination. "No…" Jordan said, "I'm not going to panic."

"Good." Chalcie reached over the edge of the tub and began to massage his chest gently with the towel. She noticed that his nipples crinkled as she touched him, and he exhaled softly, as if he'd been holding his breath in anticipation of what she was about to do to him.

She washed his chest, taking special care to make certain that she ran the wet towel over his stomach. The gentlest touch, the most delicate tracing of her fingers across his skin, and she watched as his muscles tightened with anticipation.

Her hand slipped lower in the water, and he moved back until his skin scraped against the rough sides of the tub. He couldn't believe she was going to continue in the direction that her hand was taking her. Was she so innocent that she didn't know what she was doing?

Chalcie pulled the cloth out of the water and rinsed it before she rubbed it with soap again. She had seen him pull away from her and was disappointed. Didn't he want her to touch him there? She thought all men liked that, and she was trying to please him.

"Put your head forward and I'll wash your hair and rinse with some more hot water. I don't want you to get any more chilled than you already are," Chalcie said.

Obediently he leaned forward and she worked her fingers through his hair, massaging his scalp with quick easy movements. A rinse with more water, and he began to relax again. He was certain she hadn't really meant to do what she threatened. She poured the last of the water over his back and picked up the cloth which she had placed over the side of the tub.

Without warning she reached downward, into the water, and began to wash the area below his belly button. He stared at her in shocked amazement. He hadn't expected this. Not at all!

Chalcie looked down and smothered a laugh. Maybe Johnny Tong's potion wasn't going to be necessary after all. She could already see the reaction that she'd anticipated taking place.

She stared for a moment. He was big, larger than she'd remembered. For a moment she wondered if there was enough water in the bath to keep him covered and warm if he continued to grow.

Chalcie knew that she should have been embarrassed and shy, but this was her husband and she was in a battle to make him consider her as a real woman, not a little girl who needed to be pushed aside when he wanted to play adult games.

She let her fingers move lower, encircling the shaft and rubbing the towel along the length of him. Jordan moaned and pushed upward slightly.

"Damn, woman, you'd better watch what you're doing or there's going to be hell to pay."

"Hell to pay? In what way?" Chalcie purred as she ran the cloth over every inch of him, using the rough texture to bring out the most exquisite sensations.

Jordan grabbed her hand.

"That's enough. If you do anything else, I'm going to embarrass myself and you, too," he said harshly. Jordan stood up, the water cascading off him as he reached for the old blanket that she had placed on the kitchen stump chair.

He was even more magnificent that she had thought, Chalcie realized. She almost moaned as he covered himself up. She had expected him to become excited—that was the reason she'd carried on the way she had with the cloth. But she hadn't expected to become so bothered herself. Her legs were wobbly, and she was acutely conscious of every inch of her own skin. She wanted to be touched herself. She wanted to feel that wonderfully male body against her own.

"We didn't wash your back..." she said as he marched over to the chair that had been padded with blankets and settled down in comfort.

"I don't think we need to go any further," Jordan said. Underneath the blanket, she could still see the telltale protuberance that meant he had responded to her just as she had planned.

She served him a plate of food and then brought her own plate over and sat beside him. Taffy meowed at their feet, and both of them shared bits from the meat pie with the cat.

Jordan finished the meat and gravy and leaned back.

"I don't think I could eat another bite," he said lazily. "Maybe we could save whatever else you have for tomorrow morning. After being out all night and freezing my butt all day, I'm ready for bed."

Chalcie stared at him, stricken. He had to eat at least a little of the apple dumpling. She didn't know how Johnny Tong's herbs and spices worked, but she was almost certain that sitting overnight wouldn't enhance their efficacy.

"Just a little of the dumpling?" she enticed him, spooning the rich golden syrup over the fruit and sweet crust.

Jordan protested again and then tasted the concoction. He bit into the apple slices and savored the sauce. His teeth crunched into the crisp crust and he sighed over the spices.

"This is the best dumpling I've ever tasted. Your fortune shouldn't come from running a bar—you should be cooking meals for a select few clients. I'd be the first one to pay you for this kind of food," Jordan said as he ate the rest of the dumpling.

Chalcie watched in amazement as he held out the plate for another one, and obviously was contemplating a third.

"No, that's enough," he said regretfully. "But I am glad that you didn't freeze to death in the storm last night or I'd never have known such pleasure."

Chalcie nodded. She wasn't thinking of the pleasure that he had from eating. She was waiting for the herbal remedy to make its effects known. Why hadn't she thought to ask how long it would be before he felt the urgings caused by the herbs and spices. Once he did, she had an idea that both of them would share a little pleasure.

Chalcie picked up the plates and set them into the small wash pan that had been heating with water on top of the stove.

"Why don't you take a bath as long as the water is in and it's still a little warm. I wasn't so dirty that you can't use it again, you know," Jordan said. His eyes were hooded and his voice was low and sensual.

"I…" Chalcie tried to think of a good reason why she shouldn't take a bath. She loved baths. She loved being in the water. More than that, if the herbs and spices began to work on Jordan and he suddenly became lustful and rampant, she would like to think that her body was fresh and sweet enough for him to enjoy.

The very thought made her feel faint with desire.

"Go ahead, into the bedroom, and I'll take a bath, then," Chalcie said.

Jordan cocked an eyebrow at her and smiled. "You mean you're going to take it alone? No, dear wife, it doesn't work that way. You bathed me, now I have a chance to return the favor."

Chalcie blushed. She could feel the red rising in her face. She had been certain that nothing could disturb her, but he'd managed with just those few words.

Jordan rose and let the blanket slip from around him. "The potion's working" was Chalcie's immediate thought as she looked at his naked splendor.

"Turn around," he ordered. It took him only a few seconds to undo the buttons that had taken Chalcie ten minutes to fasten. She felt each one loosen and the dress begin to slide off her shoulders. His hands were hot on her skin, removing the sleeves and tugging at the cloth around her breasts.

"Here—" He turned her around again, and his hands were on her bare breasts, his thumbs running over her nipples. He pulled the dress the rest of the way down, then the petticoat that she had put on. Within a few seconds she was standing naked in front of him. She should have been shy, she should have been shocked, but instead she was proud. She liked the way that Jordan stared at her, his dark eyes sparkling as he looked at her body.

She had been worried that he would find her repulsive. She wasn't tall and slender and blond like so many of the fancy ladies who had come to the mines. She was short and buxom and even had a few muscles here and there that came with lifting and bending and moving heavy crates and boxes.

"You're beautiful," Jordan said. He moved even closer, and suddenly there was no room between them. She could feel him, all of him, and the shock of his body against hers was almost enough to make her faint with lust. She noticed that there didn't seem to be a safe place to put her hands while he held her. She finally let them rest on his waist.

"Darling, if you want me, you have to touch me. Someone once said that lovers' hands should never be idle, and I believe that he or she was probably right." He began to rub his hands over her lightly, and every place that he touched flamed with newfound nerve endings that made her want him even more.

"Into the bath, now, and I'll help." He picked her up with no effort at all and lowered her into the water. It was still warm, and she was dizzy with excitement and desire. He picked up the cloth and ran it over the soap, then began to wash her back slowly, in even circles.

"We'll do your back first, since my own didn't get scrubbed. I'd hate for you to come out of the bath only half-clean, the way I did," Jordan said.

She relaxed against the movement of the cloth.

"I was going to wash your back. You're the one who jumped up out of the bath saying that I'd be sorry if we did anything more," Chalcie reminded him wickedly.

Jordan didn't answer, but suddenly his hands were on her breasts, and the cloth was rubbing her in places that she hadn't thought had any feelings at all. She sat up in the bath, and water splashed out, wetting Jordan's legs.

"Watch what you get wet, Chalcie. What would happen if something melted?"

Chalcie looked over the edge of the tub, assured herself that everything was still properly placed and excited and looked back up at him.

"It's not melting. Are you certain it isn't like a sponge that grows when water is added?"

Jordan didn't answer, but this time his hands went lower, across her stomach muscles and then between her legs.

Chalcie gasped and closed her legs convulsively, trapping Jordan's hands where she had never thought to let a man touch her.

"You can hold me there if you want, Chalcie, or we can finish cleaning you and take ourselves off to bed. Either way, I'm going to enjoy it," Jordan said lazily.

Slowly Chalcie opened her legs and, blushing, allowed

him access to every bit of aching, tingling flesh. He washed for a few moments and then withdrew his hand.

She felt like crying, the feeling of loss was so great.

"Now, out of there and off to bed," Jordan said. He pulled her up and walked across the room to pick up the blanket that he had shed.

He wrapped it around himself first and then reached out and enfolded Chalcie. They were bare skin to bare skin, wet to dry, cool to warm. Chalcie felt him pushing against her and she wanted to open up to him right then and there, standing in the middle of the kitchen.

"Jordan, maybe we'd better go into the bedroom," she mumbled, more interested in kissing him on the nipple again to see the funny way that it crinkled when she did. She'd wanted him long enough, now she was going to have him. She didn't care if it was Johnny Tong's potion that finally broke through Jordan's reserve and made him want to make love to her. She was past caring about anything except having him make her his real wife.

Jordan took the blanket and rubbed her to dry her off—and found even more places to touch her than he had in the bath. She didn't think it was possible to become more aroused until he rubbed against her, drying not only with the blanket but with his body.

"I think it's time," he said, and picked her up in his arms to carry her to the bed.

"Off, cat," he ordered Taffy as he maneuvered Chalcie through the doorway and placed her gently on the fur blanket, which he had already spread on the bed.

Taffy glowered at him and then stalked off the bed. She was used to being included in everything. It was obvious that she didn't understand why she couldn't take part in this particular family meeting.

"On the fur?" Chalcie asked, surprised.

"Yes, in memory of the time I should have and didn't," Jordan answered.

He lay down beside her and reached over to touch her

breasts again. She was breathing rapidly, and what he had thought at first was a blush seemed to be a permanent color to her face. Gently he took her hand and placed it on himself.

Chalcie rolled over and buried her face in his chest, but she didn't loosen her grip on the newfound plaything.

"Now, explore to your heart's content," Jordan said. "I want you to be comfortable with me, because we're going to be married a long time, and I like making love. It would be terrible if you didn't share the same passions."

Chalcie nodded but still couldn't bring herself to look at him. Instead, she contented herself with exploring the whole area with her fingers. She felt the tension building between them, and the need to hold him closer grew more and more insistent.

"Jordan…what do I do now?" Chalcie asked. Her face flamed red, but she had to find out what was next. She had a good idea, she wasn't completely without knowledge, but she'd never done it herself.

"Let me guide you," Jordan said. Gently he placed her on her back, kissing her breasts again as he did so. He licked her softly, and she responded with a moan of sheer enjoyment.

Jordan caressed her stomach, then continued downward until he touched her legs. She opened to him, letting him tease her as he readied her to accept him.

Chalcie could feel his manhood against her, and she delighted in moving herself against him. This was what she wanted, this was what she had dreamed about and fought for. Jordan was hers.

Jordan felt her heat and knew that she was ready for him. There was no false modesty, nothing that couldn't be shared between them.

"This might hurt. I'll go slow," he said softly as he lowered himself and began to press inward to make her his own.

"Hurry…" Chalcie gasped. She had wanted this for so

long that she didn't think she could wait another instant to find out what it was like to have Jordan make love to her.

The first sensation was one of fullness instead of pain, and then she surged ahead, leading him. It was exquisite torture as she felt herself rising to meet him, delighting in every inch of their bodies as they melded together.

As they moved in unison, Chalcie thought she couldn't stand the pleasure anymore, it was too much for one human being to encompass. She almost fainted from the ecstasy. For the first time, she understood that Juanita hadn't been joking when she said it was so wonderful that it felt as if there were fireworks lighting every bit of her body.

She exploded with pleasure. Never had she thought it could be like this. She led him toward the final bliss until they both sighed with satisfaction.

Jordan lay back against the pillows and smiled down at her.

"And that, my beauty, is what making love is all about," he said. He ran his hand over her body again, reveling in the softness of her skin and the slight sheen of sweat that completion had left on her breasts.

All his, he thought. All his and no one would ever take her away from him.

Chalcie smiled and let her hand trail down to the area between his legs. It wasn't that she wanted to make love again right away; she simply wanted to assure herself that he wasn't ashamed of anything that she had done with him.

Jordan smiled and then closed his eyes, drifting off to sleep.

Chalcie grinned in satisfaction. She had done it. She had managed to seduce him and now he was truly hers. She'd make the best of the marriage, but at least she had a marriage to make the best of. Though she was certain that her father would never have expected things to turn out this way, he had done her the best possible turn he could have by forcing her to marry Jordan.

She nuzzled against his shoulder, and he awoke, half-startled, to stare at her. For a moment he'd thought it was a dream.

He caught her left hand and looked down at the bare fingers, then frowned.

"Didn't you like the present?" he asked, and his voice was like that of a child who has given something that hasn't been accepted.

Chalcie looked at him, perplexed. She was tired and sated. She didn't know what he was talking about, unless he didn't realize that she loved the present of loving that he'd given her.

Jordan saw her expression and pulled himself up in bed to a sitting position.

"What did you do with the small yellow packet that was on the table?"

"There wasn't anything on the table. I'm certain, because I scrubbed it and then mixed all the ingredients for dinner right there." She was beginning to feel warm and excited again. He'd left her a present?

Jordan frowned. "Was there anything on the table that it might have been swept into?"

Chalcie thought. The table had been bare except for a candle lamp and Taffy.

"Taffy!" Chalcie exclaimed. "When I came in, she was on the table and I shooed her off. I think she was carrying something yellow in her mouth, but I didn't take the time to look for it. There were other things on my mind," she said, blushing. "I'll look in her favorite sleeping place."

Chalcie was gone for a few moments before she started to scream.

"Jordan, come here, come quick, look!"

"Is it the ring? Is something wrong?"

Jordan bolted out of the bed and ran into the outer room, stopping short as he looked at the cat on the soft blanket that served to make his chair cozy and comfortable. Taffy was asleep on the most comfortable chair in the house.

Chalcie scratched Taffy on top of the head, and as the

cat leaned forward, she disturbed the old blankets that cushioned the chair. The small yellow envelope that had been hiding in a crack of the chair fell to the floor at Chalcie's feet.

Jordan swooped down and tried to take the envelope before Chalcie could reach it. Chalcie's hand closed over the envelope and she turned it over to read the inscription.

She looked up at Jordan and smiled. "I love you, too, and there's nothing more to be forgiven. We're starting over.

"Now, can I open this? I love presents!" She ripped the little envelope open and there, in her hand, lay the ring.

"Oh, Jordan…"

"It's a wedding ring. I felt awful bad about not having one to give you the night we were married, and then things didn't go right.…" He was staring down at the floor, almost afraid to meet her eyes. "Do you like it?"

He had commissioned it especially for Chalcie. The body of the ring was made with gold from his own mine. The roses that had been carved around the stone were to symbolize her sweetness, and the ruby was for the fire that made her so special to him.

"It's beautiful. I've always been partial to rubies…but how did you know?" Chalcie asked. She was certain they'd never talked about gemstones. At least not that she could remember.

"I decided to get something that would match your hair—and your temper. Every time it flashes, down through the years, it'll remind everyone to watch out for that disposition of yours!"

Chalcie looked up at him and then put her hands on her hips and cocked her head to one side. "And what do you mean by that remark, Mr. de Chatain? Are you telling me that I'm not sweet and pliant and even-tempered?"

"Even-tempered, yes. Always angry, kind of like a flash fire!"

"Those are fighting words!" She advanced on him and

began to run her hand over his chest again. She'd show him fire, but of a kind that he had never seen before. The first time had been fine, but the second and from now on…oh, the grand times they would have! Then, abruptly, she stopped.

"Something wrong?"

"Yes. I want you to put this on my finger. I need to feel really, properly married," Chalcie said. She handed him the ring and he obliged, slipping the golden circle on her finger.

Chalcie leaned forward to kiss him again, but he drew back. Disappointed, she stared at him, wondering if she'd done something wrong.

"I almost forgot, with the rush of things. A letter came in for you today. I brought it home."

Chalcie gasped. A letter? There was only one possible reason for receiving a letter.

Jordan handed her the thin paper packet and she looked at it, tracing her name and the address that had been given. She was almost afraid to open it. What if her grandparents never wanted to hear from her again? What if they were both dead and this was from someone else?

"Aren't you going to open it?" Jordan asked.

Chalcie nodded and reached for her knife to slit the paper.

Our dearest granddaughter,
We cannot tell you how happy we are to finally have word that you are alive and well and safe. We have tried for years to find you but always seemed to reach the place that you had just been. Our lives have been very lonely without you, but we rejoice in your marriage and hope and pray that you will be able to come back to Boston one day soon to see us and your cats. Your grandfather and I await your next letter with great delight and hope.

Grandma and Grandpa

Chalcie held the letter close and this time she let the tears flow.

"I'm sorry, Chalcie, I thought it would be good news," Jordan said. He reached out to hold her and she went willingly to him.

"It's not bad news. On the contrary, I have everything I could ever want. Having Taffy and you and the ring and the letter is more than I ever dared hope for."

"I'm only second on that list?"

"Work harder," Chalcie said, "and with a little more practice at night, I'm certain you could move into first place very soon!"

Chapter Eighteen

Eduardo walked slowly through the night toward the C.K., when he saw two men standing in the deepening dusk at the edge of Chinese Camp. His attention was drawn to the men because they were skulking around, acting as if they didn't want anyone to notice that they were in the area.

"Now, what do you suppose those men are doing there on a cold night like this?" he said aloud as he hugged the shadows and advanced on them. The sounds of Sonora faded, and the distinctly different sounds of the camp became more clear as he followed the rocky trail. He pulled his coat up around his ears to keep the cold wind from cutting through to the bone.

"Watch it," one of the men said when he was only twenty feet from them. They grabbed the small candle they had been using and doused it, sliding into the darkness and eluding Eduardo.

When Eduardo reached the rocks, there was no sign of the men. He had, however, had a chance to get a good look at them.

But it couldn't be. Pete Ames was dead, wasn't he? Eduardo thought back to what Juanita had told him about Chalcie's escape the day before she married Jordan. She had left Pete Ames for dead.

He leaned against the rocks and waited for another sound that would tell him where the men had disappeared. He wanted to have a chance to talk to this blond stranger.

Eduardo shook his head. It wasn't a nightmare; he was too damned cold to be asleep. The obvious explanation was that the man simply looked like Ames. And he hadn't had all that good a look at the man, anyway, with the darkness and the feeble light of the candle. Still, he had been talking to Tourelle; Eduardo was certain of that, even in the candlelight. And Tourelle had a reputation for being a man who didn't care how he won, just as long as he did win.

Tourelle and Ames? A nasty combination, if it was true.

A chill ran down Eduardo's spine. If Pete Ames was back, Juanita and Chalcie could both be in danger. Better to warn them both and have it be a false alarm than to wait and endanger his beloved Juanita and her friend.

"Are you certain?" she asked him. Eduardo nodded. He knew trouble when he saw it, and he'd seen blond, tall and blue-eyed trouble at the edge of town, talking to Jordan's partner, Tourelle.

"Take over the bar," Juanita ordered. She flung the towel at him that she had been using to wipe the glasses and ran through the cold darkness toward Chalcie's house.

She had seen Jordan about ten minutes before as he surveyed the bar and then ducked out. He'd had the look of a satisfied Cheshire cat about him. Things were obviously going better at home. But Jordan had said something about having to check something at the Dry Gulch, and that meant that Chalcie was home alone!

What if Pete Ames found out where Chalcie was living? He could reach the house long before Juanita, and Chalcie could be dead before she even knew she was in danger. Juanita couldn't imagine what she'd do if she found Chalcie wounded or dead...her best friend gone? No, she couldn't even think about it! As she ran through the night, the images grew worse, more fearsome, more terrible. By the time she reached the house, she was almost sobbing in terror.

Juanita turned onto the small path leading to the house and saw Chalcie at the stove, cooking something for Jordan's dinner. She was safe for the moment.

"Juanita, what on earth are you doing here? I thought you'd be busy at the bar," Chalcie said as she opened the door to her friend's insistent knocking.

Juanita was gasping for air, and she almost ripped the door off the hinges as she threw it shut and dropped the heavy bar in place.

"It's Ames and Tourelle. I can't be certain that Eduardo is right, but if he is, you could be in danger. I think Ames has come back to harm you and Jordan."

"Ames? But he's dead…" Chalcie said, her stomach sinking. He was dead, wasn't he? He would have come back before this, wouldn't he?

"I hope he's dead and decomposed somewhere on that mountain, where you left him. But what if Eduardo is right?" Juanita announced as she removed her long cloak. She was sweating from panic and exertion, and the room was warm. "Keep the door shut. Close the window shutters. Do anything you can to stay safe until I can find Jordan and send him home."

"We'll both feel like fools if we're wrong," Chalcie said, biting her lip. "It could just have been someone who looks like Pete Ames talking to Tourelle, couldn't it?"

"Yes, it could have been. I thought of that myself. But why would they have been trying to keep anyone else from seeing them together? That doesn't make sense." Juanita began to pace the small room. She was too frustrated to stay still any longer. "It does make sense if they're planning something."

She paused in front of Chalcie. "Tell me, have there been any strange things happening around here lately?

Maybe some sounds that didn't fit in, or maybe you've found a lock loose when you knew you'd closed it? Anything that could give us a clue about what these men are planning, if they're out to get you and Jordan.''

"Nothing at all. And, Juanita, I don't think there was ever a chance that Ames would survive after eating those mushrooms. People die from them all the time. Look at what happened to Bobby Cox just a week ago. He ate one of the mushrooms, and even Doc Blake couldn't do anything except watch him die. There's no reason that Ames wouldn't have just sunk deeper and deeper into sleep until it was all over.''

"Tell me again exactly what happened on that mountain, because one of us has made a mistake, and if Ames is alive, he's dangerous.''

Juanita stopped pacing and sat down. She picked up the cup of tea and took a sip of the slightly bitter drink. She didn't particularly like tea, but she hoped it would settle her stomach after the fright Eduardo had given her with his news.

"I've told you before. I left Pete Ames dead in a mountain cabin. He was unconscious and slipping toward death when I took his mare and ran for my life. I've seen how that poison works before, and this time was no different,'' Chalcie said. "I know how woozy the stew made me feel after I had only a few bites of it. It would have been impossible for either of those men to eat all the stew, become unconscious and then recover. Amanita poisoning doesn't work that way. Besides, why wouldn't Ames have come back and made trouble earlier?''

"Maybe he didn't want to face being strung up for your father's murder,'' Juanita said, reminding Chalcie that Ames wouldn't be welcomed with open arms to the mining camp. "The men might not have been all that fond of your father, but they liked him more than they liked Pete Ames.

Some memories here are pretty good, and even today Pete Ames couldn't walk in here and hope to leave Sonora a free man."

Chalcie nodded. "But he could hope to come back and try some underhanded trick if he still wanted to get even with me."

"Yes, and that's why I'm warning you. Watch your step for a few weeks, until we're certain there's nothing to the sighting. I'll tell Jordan to come right home."

"Don't worry him…" Chalcie began.

"He's your husband, he needs to worry," Juanita said.

Chalcie smiled for the first time since the conversation had started. "Look what he gave me last night."

She held out her finger so that Juanita could inspect the carved roses and hearts and the fine ruby displayed in the middle of the center gold rose. "I almost didn't get the ring. Taffy had stolen the envelope and buried it in the chair, and Jordan thought I'd refused his gift." She stopped and blushed. She hadn't refused any of his gifts.

Juanita was glad that Chalcie could think for a few moments about something other than Pete Ames and the threat that he posed toward her.

"If it was such a wonderful night, why did you look like you were going to cry when I came in here?"

"I wasn't," Chalcie started to say, then she looked down at her hands and her voice faded away. "Well, I guess I was," she said so quietly that Juanita could barely hear her.

Chalcie sniffed. She wasn't going to cry. She wasn't going to tell Juanita about what she'd done. It would all work out.

She set about closing the heavy shutters that Jordan had on the inside of each window. He also had another set of iron shutters for the outside of the windows, but she wasn't going to tempt fate and the possibility of running into Pete Ames by venturing outside.

"All right, what's going on?" Juanita sighed. She knew Chalcie. Eventually she'd tell her.

Chalcie shook her head and rubbed at her eyes. "I went to Chinese Camp yesterday morning."

"That's no crime. At least you didn't see Ames and Tourelle. That could have been dangerous. And I knew you'd gone, remember. Did you get what you wanted from Johnny Tong?"

"It's not a crime, but, Juanita, I used the love potion on him last night in the apple dumplings, and then, right after that, he made love to me," Chalcie said miserably.

"And wasn't that what you wanted?" Juanita was genuinely mystified.

"Yes…" Chalcie's answer was drawn out.

"Then what on earth is the difficulty?" Juanita was beginning to lose patience with Chalcie.

"Because if he made love to me because of that damned potion, he doesn't really love me. I can't live with that now. What will I do when it wears off? He could leave me." Chalcie gulped. "He could leave me even if he loves me. He'd think I tricked him, and he'll abandon me if he ever finds out that I went to Johnny Tong and picked up that little packet and used it on him."

Juanita sat back and sighed. "If he finds out, then you'll have a problem. But why don't you wait and see what happens? Johnny Tong's potions are usually reliable. With any luck it won't stop working until he's really fallen in love with you," Juanita said, trying to comfort her friend.

Chalcie laughed bitterly at Juanita's suggestion.

"Chalcie, you have to look on the bright side," Juanita said firmly. "Do the best you can to keep him always by your side. Women can do that, you know. Please him in bed and make certain that the business doesn't go broke. With all that to keep you busy, you shouldn't have much time to worry. And by the time you have a chance to worry, Jordan will either be gone or he'll be in love with you."

"I'm being silly worrying about that potion?" Chalcie asked, her voice still wavering.

Juanita nodded. "The herbs and spices did just what you wanted them to do. They broke down that barrier that's been growing every day between you and Jordan. And you don't seem to have suffered from the effects of your first night."

Even with her eyes puffy from crying, Chalcie still had a glow about her that came from being a loved and loving woman.

"Why worry? You've got what you wanted and it's the best for both of you. Don't borrow trouble—it will come of its own accord."

Chalcie nodded. She wiped her eyes and tried valiantly to smile. "You're right. I have to worry about whatever or whoever Eduardo saw out there at the edge of town."

Juanita nodded and stood up. "I'm going to get back to the bar. I'll tell Jordan about Ames when he comes in. But, Chalcie, until he gets home, please keep the door locked, and make certain that you have something near at hand to protect you, all right? I could always send Eduardo over to stay with you, if you wanted...."

Chalcie laughed. "No, I'll be fine. Don't worry."

She closed the door behind Juanita. Potions and Pete Ames. Resolutely she put both of them out of her mind as she started to give the little house a final straightening up. She'd talk with Jordan tonight about Ames and Tourelle. Until then, she wouldn't worry. She dropped the heavy wooden latch in place and pulled in the latch string. She would just keep busy until Jordan came home. There was no point in worrying.

"There is no reason to overreact to something that probably never even happened," Chalcie said. It wasn't that she didn't believe Eduardo had seen something, but she didn't think he'd seen Ames and Tourelle together.

She had almost finished cleaning when a thump rocked the door, followed by a moan, tapering off to silence.

"What the hell was that?"

Chalcedony dusted her hands off on her apron and walked a few steps toward the heavy pine door. She was shaking with sudden fear. The memory of Juanita's warning came back to her clearly. She picked up the thin meat knife that she had used to bore holes in the chunk of venison she was cooking for the evening meal. She wasn't going to open the door without some sort of protection.

"Help me…" the moan came again.

Chalcedony bit her lower lip. It could be dangerous. What if this was a decoy, something designed to lure her to the door? What if Pete Ames had come back to town and was lying in wait to attack her if she answered the summons?

She hesitated in front of the door, afraid to open it and afraid to leave it closed in case someone really did need her help.

What if it was someone hurt? What if Jordan was on the other side of that door? Her breath caught at the very idea of something happening to Jordan. It could be Jordan and she'd never know if she didn't open the door.

"I'm coming," she said, and removed the wooden latch. Chalcie screamed as she was hit by the dead weight of the man who crashed through the door and sprawled on the floor. Blood dripped in a heavy dark stream, and she stared in horror at his ragged wounds.

"Get Jordan," the man whispered, and closed his eyes.

Chalcie stared into the darkness. She couldn't see anything, but she had the gut feeling that someone else was out there, watching.

She closed and bolted the door and pulled the man over

beside the stove. The least she could do for him was keep him warm. She turned his wounded face toward her and grimaced. She couldn't even tell who it was at the moment.

"Please," the man whispered again. Chalcie closed her eyes. If there was someone waiting outside for her, she would be dead the instant she stepped off the porch. If she stayed in the house where she was safe, the man would surely die.

Chalcie hesitated only a moment. She had to chance it. She could fetch Jordan from the bar and send someone for the doctor at the same time. If she stayed with the man, she'd never be able to save him. She was a good nurse, but not good enough to stop this kind of bleeding.

"I'll be right back. I'll bring Jordan," she assured the man, and was rewarded with a slight nod of his head. Pausing only to spread the fur blanket over him, she ran out the door toward the bar.

As she ran, Chalcie imagined that she heard footsteps behind her, and she braced for the blow that would come, knocking her again into that soundless black pit where she had been when Ames had kidnapped her. Nothing happened, though she was certain she could still hear something in the snow behind her. Her right leg began to cramp as she raced through the snow. She stumbled once, and then again, and she knew that if she went down, she wouldn't have a chance to get up again. Someone was following her. Someone who had already almost killed a man.

"Please, not now, just don't cramp now," she pleaded with her leg. She was in agony. It felt as if the muscle were tearing with every step, but she still ran. Where was Jordan? If Juanita had talked to him, why wasn't he hurrying home to take care of her?

She ran up the street and paused in front of the bar, looking for him.

The C.K. was the typical nighttime brawl of men drinking and women trying to entice them to spend their money on a romp upstairs. Chalcedony pulled back the calico and looked in, hoping she would find Jordan immediately.

"Hey, little lady…" One of the men started to proposition her, but the words died on his lips when he realized who she was.

"Find Jordan right now. If he isn't here, look at the Dry Gulch. I need him at home!"

She looked around. "And you—" She grabbed another man, who was making his way toward the bar. "You fetch the doctor and tell him to come to Jordan's house immediately."

The men didn't even pause to ask questions. They heard the urgency in her voice.

"Chalcie, why are you here?" Juanita rushed up to her friend.

"I need to find Jordan. Trouble at home," she said. She didn't dare tell Juanita more in front of the men. She'd understand that it had something to do with Tourelle and Ames.

"He just came back in about thirty seconds ago. Jordan!" Juanita roared at the top of her voice. Instantly the whole bar fell silent. When Juanita yelled, she had the power to command instant attention. "Jordan, if you're here, answer right now!"

"Here!" Jordan's voice floated over the crowd, and the men began to part as he pushed through them to reach Chalcie.

"Come on, I'll explain on the way. We've got to get home," Chalcie said. She spun and ran, not even waiting to see if Jordan was following her.

"Tell me what happened," Jordan demanded as he raced along behind her.

Chalcie was panting, but she managed to tell him the bare bones of what had happened.

"A tall, heavy, brown-haired man fell in the door and proceeded to bleed on my nice clean floor," Chalcie answered tartly as she stopped for a moment to catch her breath. "I sent someone for the doctor, but I'm not sure the man will be alive when we get back to the house. He was that bad."

Jordan grabbed her arm and pulled her along. "Damn it, what did he look like?"

"Like most of his face had been shot away. He's big, and about twenty-five, but I can't even guess any more than that," Chalcie said, struggling to keep up with him as he ran.

"No name?"

"Not that he could tell me," Chalcie said.

Jordan sprinted for the door and wrenched it open. He skidded to a stop in front of the man.

Chalcie saw him sway slightly as he looked at the man's gouged face. Jordan's complexion was suddenly chalky white and he swallowed several times convulsively.

"Jimmy? What the hell happened?" Jordan reached down and touched the man's shoulder.

From somewhere deep inside himself, Jimmy summoned enough strength to open his eyes.

"Tourelle…" Jimmy croaked, and closed his eyes.

"Tourelle? Tourelle did this to you?" Jordan's voice was low and urgent. "Damn it, man, he's my partner, why would he do this?"

"Watch out. Tourelle and Ames. He jumped the claim…taking everything as his own…you're being robbed by high grading anyway…" Jimmy was gasping between each fragment of information.

"What's going on? What the hell happened to this man? Looks like a bear got him." The doctor that Chalcie had sent for stomped into the room, bringing with him the smell of the fresh storm brewing.

"Looks like he was shot at close range with a shotgun to me," Chalcie said. She had already set out the rags that the doctor would need to clean the wound. She had some strips of cloth browning in the pan at the back of the heater. If the man survived, the sterilized cloth could be used for packing the wound. The whiskey, good for cleaning as well as a painkiller, was ready for both the doctor and the patient.

The doctor winced. It was one of the worst gunshot wounds he'd seen, outside of the time Larry Tomlinson tripped over his own rifle. Larry had died, and it didn't look all too good for this poor sod's survival, either.

"Hell, can't hurt to give it a try," the doctor said.

"Don't…hurts too much. I don't care, just let me sleep…get Tourelle…" Jimmy said. He didn't even open his eyes one last time before he died.

Chalcie turned away from the sight, blindly burying her face against Jordan's chest. She shook with shock and had to fight the urge to start screaming and never stop. She wasn't equipped to handle a man dying in the middle of her kitchen.

"Jordan, want the body taken out to the shed?" the men asked.

She felt Jordan nod and heard the grunting as the men lifted Jimmy and carried him out into the snow.

Jordan held Chalcie, his warmth comforting her as it had on the mountain, until she stopped shaking.

"Chalcie, I've got to go. I'm sorry about this. I'd rather stay and take care of you. Hell, I'd rather stay here and make love to you all night, but I can't." He whispered the last, a special warm message only for her ears. "I can't allow Tourelle to get away with this murder. He's got to be stopped."

"What do you mean? You're not going after him, are you?" Chalcie held on to Jordan's coat, her fingers refusing to let go. "You can't leave me alone. Jimmy says that Tourelle is working with Ames, and if it's true, he's going to be after you and me, too."

"You left Ames dead on the mountain. Jimmy was hallucinating about that. No, Chalcie, this is between Tourelle and me. He won't try to hurt you."

"Send someone else," Chalcie pleaded, abandoning all pretense of being brave.

"I can't send anyone else to stop Tourelle. Besides, I think I'm going to enjoy gunning down the bastard. I liked Jimmy and he didn't deserve to die like this. Jimmy would have liked to die in bed with a woman, enjoying himself. Not bleeding to death on a kitchen floor."

Gently Jordan loosened Chalcie's hands. He wished with all his heart that he could have stayed with her. The scent of her hair and the softness of her body against his caused an instant physical reaction.

"I'll send someone back to take care of you. I won't leave you by yourself. Just wait for Tom from the Dry Gulch to come, and don't unlock the door to anyone else except Eduardo or Juanita."

"Stay here and take care of me. Jordan, the pass isn't open to the mine. You know that. And even if it has started to thaw, it's so treacherous that you'll be killed. Please, Jordan, stay here. I couldn't bear it if something happened to you!" Chalcie pleaded with him.

"You don't know how I'd like to stay. But I can't," Jordan said. "I think you'll be safe. If Ames really is around, he wouldn't dare try anything in town. There are too many other people around."

"So you're going to go where the danger is? You're deliberately going to face Tourelle at the mine? You're crazy!" Chalcie was arguing with all her heart. She didn't want to become a widow after only one night of love. That would have been too cruel.

"I'm sorry, Chalcie. I've got to get up to that mine and find out what's going on. First I'll take care of Tourelle, then I'll be back.... Wait for me, please?" There was a note of pleading in his voice as he kissed her once lightly on the lips.

"Forever."

Her hands reached out to catch him back to her, to keep him at her side, where he belonged. She caught nothing but empty air.

Chalcie stood in the kitchen and felt the sensation of his lips on hers, and the fading warmth.

Chapter Nineteen

Chalcie stared into the darkness. She could still hear the fading sound of the horse's hooves as Jordan left her.

It was a mistake for Jordan to try to go up to the mine. It was dark and slippery on the trail and he was going alone. If something happened, she'd never know until it was too late to help.

Damn him anyway. Why was he worrying her like this? Jimmy was already dead. It wasn't as if hurrying off to the mine were going to change that fact. And if Tourelle and his men were really up there, holding fort on the mine, Jordan was still going to have to come back down the trail, hire men to go up with him and mount an assault later.

Fighting Tourelle now was sheer folly!

Chalcie stood staring into the darkness and thought of all the things she should have said to try to discourage Jordan. It was too late now to do anything, but she still thought Jordan was wrong even to attempt to go up to the mine. She knew it deep in her bones, but there had been nothing specific, no real reason that she could have argued with him to stay in Sonora. It was just a gut feeling that he was in danger.

"Chalcie, what happened? I left as soon as I could… The men said something about a doctor?" Juanita rushed up to the front door, arriving just before Chalcie locked it.

"You've missed all the excitement," Chalcie said as she led the way into the kitchen. She stepped carefully around the pool of blood; it made her sick to look at it.

"Good Lord, what happened?" Juanita flinched as she saw the gore.

"One of the men that Jordan left at his mine came here to die. He had half his face shot off, and the only thing he could say was something about Tourelle and the mine being taken over." Chalcie gripped the back of the chair with her hands so tightly that her knuckles were white. "So naturally, Jordan had to go racing out of here heading toward the mine, where he's certain that he will have a showdown with Tourelle." Chalcie's voice betrayed the anger and despair that she felt.

"He's going up to the mine? Does he know about Ames? What if it's all a trap? What if they're trying to separate you two and then they're going to attack?"

Chalcie stared at Juanita. It was suddenly so clear, the things that she hadn't been able to tell Jordan because she hadn't had time to think them through and put all her feelings and reactions into carefully reasoned statements.

"You don't think that Ames and Tourelle could have planned an ambush, do you?" she whispered. Of course Ames and Tourelle could have been working together all this time. First they steal what they can from Jordan, and then they kill him in an ambush somewhere on the way to the mine. Once they were positive that he was dead, and thus no danger to them, the two men would double back into town.

Ames and Tourelle's dirty work wouldn't be finished with Jordan's death. They'd come back for her. Ames would still be out for revenge, she knew. The two men would expect her to be unprotected and probably blind to her own danger. They'd think it would be easy to murder her just as they had killed Jordan.

"But why all the skulking around? What's it going to get them? Jimmy didn't have any money of his own, and

Tourelle must know that Jordan won't just stand by and let him steal a whole mine.'' Juanita was pacing now, trying to follow the twisted logic of the men.

''Oh, I understand it just fine,'' Chalcie said bitterly. ''It was probably Ames's idea all along.'' It would be just the kind of plan that Ames would be capable of making, if he had managed to survive that poisoning.

''If he is alive, he's the type of man who would never rest until he had revenge,'' she went on. ''And the way he'd take revenge would be to find a way to end up with the Kent fortune, no matter how he accomplished it.''

''I still don't understand. What does that have to do with Ames and Tourelle working together?''

''Don't you see? Tourelle is Jordan's partner, and if both Jordan and I die, then Tourelle would take all the assets, wouldn't he? We have no other heirs, no one else to inherit from us. It's happened before—a partner dies, the other one takes everything.''

''Why would Tourelle share with Ames?''

''Either Ames thought of the plan, or Tourelle doesn't really intend to share and thinks he can kill Ames off after he's extracted all the help he can from the man. If that's what Tourelle is thinking, I feel sorry for him, because Ames will shoot him in the back before Tourelle even knows he has a gun. That's the kind of man Ames is.''

Chalcie stopped dead in her tracks and blanched. She swayed and had to grab Juanita's arm for support.

''Oh, my God…'' Chalcie whispered.

''What is it?'' Juanita held her friend steady.

''Juanita, I need help, and fast. If we are right, then we have to catch Jordan before he leaves town. Tourelle and Ames won't go back up to the mine. They'll lie in wait somewhere along the road and Jordan will never even know he's walking into a trap.''

Chalcie's heart was thumping hard enough to make her chest ache with the pounding. Sheer terror surged through her. She didn't have time to warn Jordan. He had too much of a lead for her to catch up with him and warn him before he walked into a hail of bullets!

"Please God, keep him at the Dry Gulch for just a few minutes." If only Tom wasn't at the bar, and Jordan had to cast around for someone else to send to make certain she was safe at home. It would give her the few extra seconds that she needed to warn him of the impending ambush.

Chalcie even knew where Ames and Tourelle would almost certainly attack. Chinese Camp. The rocks where Eduardo had seen the men meeting and then couldn't find a trace of them. Tourelle and Ames would have the ambush set up there, she was almost positive. Sonora was settled, but not so settled that there weren't places to hide even at the edge of town where the men would never have been found. Hide and lie in wait for someone to come riding along, right into deadly crossfire.

It was a trap and Jordan was riding into the middle of it.

"I'm going to try and catch him. It's my only hope."

Chalcie grabbed the extra rifle and checked that it was loaded. She seized her sheathed knife and pushed it into her pocket. It wasn't much, but it was better than going into the battle totally unarmed. She flung her coat around her shoulders and raced outside.

"Juanita, go for help. Chinese Camp, that's where the trouble will be!" she yelled at her friend, who was still standing in the middle of the kitchen, trying to think what she could do to help her friend. Juanita took off at a dead run toward the bar, while Chalcie headed for the corral.

"Come on, mare, come over here and I'll give you a wonderful carrot when we get back," she pleaded with the horse. There wasn't time to play around with the saddle or bridle. It would have to be bareback or nothing. With any luck she'd keep her seat even over the treacherous terrain that lay between her and the camp.

The mare, sensing Chalcie's panic, came trotting over,

and Chalcie jumped up on the mounting block that Jordan had placed at the gate for her. The horse stood still as Chalcie mounted. She leaned over, grasped the mane and unlocked the corral gate.

"Come on, girl, we're in a real fight, and there's no time to lose," she said as she urged the horse toward Chinese Camp. She almost lost her balance as she pulled herself back up and tried to juggle the rifle and still keep her grip on the horse's hair. Somewhere in the distance she heard shots, and she began to whimper.

"Please, not Jordan," she prayed. The tears were freezing on her cheeks and she didn't even dare lift her hand to rub them off. She might slip off the horse, or worse, she might lose the rifle and, with it, any chance to stop the men before they shot Jordan.

How much time did she have? One minute? Thirty seconds to catch up with Jordan and help him? What if there wasn't enough time to do anything to stop them?

"No, I won't think of that," Chalcie said stubbornly.

Still, she couldn't wipe the worry from her mind. What if she was too late? A horrible image of Jordan sprawled on the cold rocks, his face blown away as Jimmy's had been, flashed in front of her eyes and she moaned. If Ames and Tourelle harmed Jordan, she'd hunt them down to the ends of the earth. They wouldn't have to come searching for her, they'd have to run to keep away from her vengeance.

Chalcie raced through town, shouting inquiries to anyone she passed hoping that Jordan was still in Sonora.

No one had seen him.

Chalcie leaned forward, trying to spot the rocks that led to Chinese Camp. It was too dark to see much, and the horse had slowed to a crawl because the snow and ice were so treacherous. She could hear what sounded like horse's hooves ahead of her, but she didn't even dare hope that it was Jordan. And where were the other people? Surely Juanita should have had time to get some of the men out of the bar and onto the trail.... Why couldn't she hear them?

She looked upward and prayed for a break in the clouds and moonlight to show her what was ahead of her. As if in answer to the words, the clouds parted and the moonlight, frail and fragile though it was, lighted the way for her.

The road began to rise, and the rocks that formed the small pass between Sonora and the Chinese camp closed on either side of her.

She strained to see something, anything that would give her a clue about how close she was to Jordan. Then, finally, a movement. There, ahead of her, she could see something, but not on the trail itself. It was something on the highest point of the rocks, where the trail led into a narrow ravine and then out again into the camp.

Chalcie saw the slight movement again, and the figures came into focus. Two men were on the top of the highest rocks. Chalcie stared at them. The shock hit her with a physical force. Both men were holding rifles, and they were pointing downward, right toward her.

No, one was aimed toward her, and the other was leveled at a point ahead of her. At Jordan.

Suddenly Jordan rounded a small turn in the road, and she could see him. She saw the men shift, moving the sights of their rifles, and she knew that she could save Jordan or she could save herself.

With only the rifle, she would never be able to shoot twice and kill both of the men. There was only one chance of making the men forget Jordan and drawing the fire to herself so he had a chance to survive the deadly ambush. She had to draw both of them, make them fire on her and forget, for even a second, to watch for Jordan. She knew Jordan; he'd hear shots and would dive for cover. He'd be safe, and suddenly the only thing in her life that was important was for Jordan to live.

Chalcie let the mare move slowly forward, pretending

that she hadn't seen the men on the rocks above her. Her fingers tightened on the metal trigger of the gun, and she prayed that the shooting skill that she had learned from the Mexicans would still be fine enough to let her kill a man without having time to really aim.

The men shifted their stance, and she could see them tensing, obviously waiting until the perfect moment to loose their volley of shots. She and Jordan were about to die.

Chalcie leaned back, holding on to the mane with one hand and gripping the rifle with her other. She had only one chance, one shot, one moment left to live and to save Jordan before she was blasted by the men above her.

Chalcie threw her head back in defiance and screamed. It was a high ululating challenge, primitive and barbaric. It rode over the rocks, rebounded from the highest points and filled the small valley that she was riding in. The wind swept it upward, and there was a startling, growling cry answered by a coyote, and then by a mountain lion who had been prowling the area. Together, Chalcie and the animals' voices melded as she challenged Tourelle and Ames.

Tourelle and Ames jumped and spun, trying to find the source of the unearthly keening that surrounded them, bouncing off the walls and echoing back against them. It was like nothing they had ever heard before or ever wanted to hear again.

Then, in one swift movement, she brought the rifle up to her shoulder, let loose of the horse's mane so she could use her other hand to steady the gun, and shot upward. It worked as it had worked hundreds of times in the hot Mexican desert. One man took the blast squarely, flying back from the rock. She could see the other man on top of the rocks raising his rifle again, pointing toward her, and she braced for the shock of the blast that would kill her. There was no time and no place to run.

Her shriek died in the wind, and the second man tightened his finger on the trigger. Though it was barely a second since she had fired, every increment of time stretched and lengthened. Abruptly the man twitched and slapped at his back. The rifle flew upward, and he pitched forward, landing on the rocks and sliding down the face until he tumbled into a heap almost at Jordan's feet. A small avalanche of rubble followed him down to the base of the rock.

Jordan stared at the man. He was still shaking from the cry that had cut through the ravine, and then the blast from an unseen rider behind him that had cut down a man he hadn't even seen. He wasn't dumb, he knew an ambush when he saw one, but he still hadn't put all the pieces together. Who was above him? And who the hell was the second man who had landed almost at his feet?

Jordan jumped down from the horse and advanced on the figure, his rifle at the ready. He prodded the man with the cold metal. There was no response. The man was dead, though Jordan couldn't see a single wound on his body that would account for the fact that he had ceased to breathe.

Chalcie sat still for a moment and then, belatedly realizing that she was still alive, she grabbed the mare's mane again and urged her horse forward. The only shot fired had been her own. That meant that Jordan was still alive, didn't it? The earlier shots didn't mean anything, did they?

"Please, Jordan, be alive!" Chalcie whispered as she urged the mare the last fifty feet to the bend in the trail.

Jordan heard the horse behind him and turned, his rifle at the ready, as Chalcie rounded the curve. She could see him tense, his finger on the trigger, then relax as he realized who had been following him.

"Chalcie, what the hell is going on?" Jordan ran toward her. Chalcie let herself slide off the mare and into his arms.

"It was a trap," she said, burying her face in his chest and taking deep breaths of his scent to assure herself that he was indeed alive and holding her. "It was a trap, and I didn't realize it until Juanita and I talked after you'd left. I knew what Tourelle was doing. He was going to kill you."

Jordan nodded and pulled her even closer to him. "It

was a pretty good plan. He almost carried it off, and me with it.''

Chalcie shuddered. "Then I thought, if Tourelle and Ames are actually partners, then Ames would win after all, if both of us were dead. Tourelle would get everything you owned, because he was your partner, and he'd split it with Ames.''

"So you came to rescue me," Jordan said quietly. Now he understood the eerie scream that had flooded the rocks and crevices. She had seen the men and had drawn the fire toward herself to save him. It was her shot that had killed whoever was up there on the rock. Any doubts he had ever had about Chalcie and her love for him were quietly put to rest.

"Chalcie, do me the honor of staying as my wife for the rest of my life, will you?" Jordan said as he smoothed her hair and kissed her again.

Chalcie smiled. "Why?''

"Because I'd hate to have you for an enemy, that's why. You are one of the most dangerous women I've ever had the privilege of meeting. I'd hate to have you mad at me— I'm not certain I'd survive!''

"Never angry with you..." Chalcie said dreamily, and then, realizing what she was saying, she laughed. "Well, maybe angry, but not enough to do anything terrible.''

Jordan groaned. "I'll try and stay in your good graces. Crack shot, handy woman with poisons, even if the mushrooms didn't do the job completely, and a good businesswoman besides? These remaining years could be downright exciting!''

"Jordan, I only shot one man. Where is the other one, and why did he just fall down without ever trying to pull the trigger? He had me in his sights, I know he did." Chalcie finally regained her senses enough to think beyond the wonderfully warm feeling of Jordan holding her close.

"He's over there." Jordan pointed to the bundle of clothing at the horse's feet.

Chalcie took a step toward him and then jumped back and squeaked in surprise as another man stepped from the shadows.

"No, miss, do not worry. I am not one of those who wanted to kill you." Mr. Tong stepped forward and leaned toward the prone body. He used his cane to move the dead man so that his face could be seen.

Chalcie fought for composure as she saw the hated handsome face of Pete Ames.

"Is he dead?" she whispered.

Mr. Tong nodded. He balanced himself on his cane and reached toward the man's back. Chalcie could see nothing but what looked like a piece of straw sticking to Ames's shirt.

"He is dead. No man survives this," Mr. Tong said, displaying the straw.

"A poisoned dart?"

Mr. Tong nodded. "I had heard the men planning. I knew what they were going to do." He looked at them sagely. "Most white men I would ignore. They can kill each other if they want. But they are not going to kill the lady with the pretty brown slippers and my friend Jordan."

"How did you know what they were going to do, though?" Chalcie asked.

Mr. Tong made a face. "They talked in front of me. They think no Chinese can understand them when they plan things. They drink my tea and plot against my friends. I had to stop them." Then he turned directly toward Chalcie and bowed. "You have a fine warrior's cry. Even I was frightened."

He turned and walked away into the darkness, taking the poison dart with him.

"Chalcie, Jordan, where are you? Is everyone all right? We heard shots!" Juanita and Eduardo, closely followed by several other miners, rushed up the rock-strewn path.

"We're here. Everything is all right. Ames and Tourelle are dead," Jordan called out.

"I like that! Two men dead and he says it's all right," Juanita said, shivering.

"Would you rather it be both of us dead and Ames hoisting a whiskey in our memory?" Jordan challenged Juanita.

"No, and you know it. Now let's get on home. It's been a hell of a night. Chalcie needs some comforting." Juanita turned and started back down the path. The two men who were dead could stay there until morning. The miners would hear about the shoot-out and the bodies, and they'd appoint a squad to come out and clean up the remains.

Chalcie sagged against Jordan.

It was too much. She was going to go home and go to sleep and then, sometime tomorrow, she would confess her secret and Jordan could decide whether he wanted to stay with her or not.

Chapter Twenty

Chalcie woke and stared into the darkness. She and Jordan lay like two spoons, the warmth from one replenishing the warmth of the other. She could feel his breath on the nape of her neck, and his hand pulled her close, holding her possessively around her waist so she couldn't slip away from him in the middle of the night. She could feel every inch of him, and she took joy in his every breath. Ames and Tourelle were dead, instead of her beloved Jordan.

Today she would have to tell him. Today she might be back in her little room by the C. K. Saloon. Even with Ames and Tourelle dead, she might still finish her day without a man in love with her or a penny to her name. Chalcie reached out and pulled Taffy toward her.

She arose before Jordan and slipped out into the kitchen. She grabbed the dark red woolen dress from the clothes that she had set aside to be washed when there was a clear day. She couldn't stand to dress in the same clothes that she had been wearing the night before. Within an hour she had the fire going and water heating for tea and for the porridge she had discovered, to her horror, Jordan actually liked to eat every morning.

She heated a second container of water and set about scrubbing the floor where the blood had dried overnight. She had been so tired and so terrified when she came home after the encounter with Ames and Tourelle that she hadn't had the strength even to think about cleaning away the blood.

She had cooked the porridge and was on her hands and knees, scrubbing, when she heard a knock at the door.

Chalcie sat back on her heels and looked at the door. Should she answer it? The thought of yet another terror lurking there almost made her ignore the sound.

"Chalcie, I know you're awake. I saw the light, even if you haven't opened the blinds. Come on, let me in." Juanita's voice came through the door, breathless and happy.

Chalcie sighed in relief. No more terrors, just Juanita. She threw the door open and embraced her friend. "You have no idea how glad I am to see you. Come in and you can watch while I scrub the floor. Would you like some tea?"

Chalcie drew her into the warmth. She closed the door into the bedroom, hoping that Jordan could sleep for a while longer. He should be able to rest, he had a clean conscience. Not like herself.

When Chalcie turned around, she got her first good look at Juanita. Her friend was glowing with happiness.

"Tell me what's happened," Chalcie said, and poured them both cups of tea.

"Eduardo asked me to marry him last night—well, this morning, after we closed the bar for a few hours."

"You *are* going to marry him, aren't you?" So that accounted for Juanita's eyes and the high color in her cheeks. It was obvious that after expecting to stay alone for the rest of her life, she had been taken by surprise at the joy of falling in love with another man.

"Of course I am. But…" The light faded gradually from Juanita's face. She turned the cup in her hands. She couldn't bring herself to look at Chalcie. She'd think her a fool for having any doubts about the match.

"What is it?" Chalcie prodded her friend into confiding. If Juanita had come this early in the morning to tell her the news, then it was obvious that she was glad to have Eduardo as her intended. But it was equally obvious that something was troubling her.

Juanita sighed. "I love Eduardo. It's not the same kind of love I had for Miguel. Nothing could ever approach that marriage. He was the perfect husband, and I cannot tell you the times I've wished that I had been allowed to die when he died."

"I know," Chalcie said quietly. She had seen Juanita cry over the wedding dress. She had heard her friend's repeated denials of ever becoming involved again with a man. She knew that for Juanita to fall in love with Eduardo had to be both frightening and exhilarating.

There had to be another problem, though. It had caused the light to leave her friend's eyes and her smile to fade. Chalcie couldn't stand to see that happen when there was no reason for it.

"Do you feel that you're being unfaithful to Miguel by falling in love with Eduardo?" There, it was out. If Juanita had not consciously thought about it, this would force her to confront the issue.

Juanita looked up, startled. "How did you know?" she whispered.

"Because I know you. I know the kind of loyalty that you have for your friends. No one else in the whole of California would have sat beside me and stitched an entire dress if they hadn't been both a good friend and loyal, even though you were certain I was wrong."

"But am I wrong to marry Eduardo?"

"No, you are not wrong. Juanita, who are you going to damage by living with this man and loving him?"

Juanita shrugged. "No one?"

"That's right. No one. Not Miguel, because awful as it is, and cruel as it may be to say this, he is dead. You're alive, Juanita. You have the same kind of needs that I do. We're both women who were content to be independent of men." Chalcie laughed. "And look where that independence got both of us—involved with men, after all."

"But I don't want to forget Miguel!"

"Has Eduardo told you never to mention Miguel's name in his presence? Has he told you that you should not think about the time that you were married to Miguel?"

Juanita shook her head. "No. He just said that if I wanted to talk, he'd listen. I think what Eduardo was really worried about was having to measure up to what Miguel was. He said that competing with a dead saint was going to be very difficult."

Chalcie set her cup of tea down and cocked her head, studying her friend.

"Do you know, I think you'd better be very careful, then."

"Why?"

"Because if you're not careful, you'll drive Eduardo away with the comparisons. Look, Juanita, Miguel was a wonderful man. But the time that he knew you and the life that you lived have passed. You have a chance to build new love and new memories with Eduardo. Don't make him feel that he is somehow less than Miguel. They're different. They aren't in competition with each other."

Juanita smiled and the light was back in her eyes. "You're right, as usual. Thank you, Chalcie. Now, will you and Jordan be able to stand up for us at a wedding? We're going to have a real *fiesta*."

"When is the wedding?" Chalcie grinned, glad to have negotiated the rocky road of giving a friend advice. More often than not, she knew, that was when most friendships foundered.

"In one week. And I think this time I'll make myself another dress. I'm not going to wear the old dreams when I have new ones. Would you like to help me sew it?" Juanita challenged Chalcie, knowing how much she disliked sewing.

"I'll help. Just give me the pretty part instead of the straight seams, all right?" Chalcie bargained.

"I'll take half the straight ones and half the fancywork, and you can do the same. But I'm still a better woman for fancywork than you are."

"Agreed. But it'll still be half and half, right?"

Juanita nodded happily.

They chatted for a few more minutes, and Juanita left to sleep a few hours before the miners descended again.

"Did I hear voices out here?" Jordan opened the door and stood in the doorway stark naked.

"Yes you did, and I suggest that if you hear voices, you'd better slip into something before you come out to greet our visitors like that," Chalcie said tartly.

"Already criticizing, are we, love? My, it was a short honeymoon, wasn't it?" Jordan said. He covered the space between them in two long steps and grabbed her, hugging her close to him. He kissed her slowly, and Chalcie could feel the fire igniting between them. Jordan was obviously and instantly ready to make love to her.

"Randy old goat! I've never seen a man who was so enthusiastic…" Chalcie said, playfully trying to pull away from him.

"And how many other men have you known like this?" Jordan scowled at her with mock anger. "How many men have held you like this and given you pleasure?" He thrust against her, heedless of the heavy woolen skirt.

"No others. You're quite enough, thank you," Chalcie said.

"Good," Jordan replied softly, and began to unbutton her dress. "You need more dresses, ones that are easier to get into. From now on, I want my woman dressed in the most beautiful clothes that I can buy."

He pulled off the dress, revealing her creamy flesh. He touched her breasts with his tongue and then kissed her, working his way up her neck until their mouths met and they tasted each other again.

"Jordan, wait. I have something to tell you," Chalcie said desperately. She couldn't let him continue to think that everything was fine between them, when she thought that it was most likely that he'd throw her out of the house the instant he knew what she'd done.

But, oh, one more time of bliss in his bed. Just one more time wouldn't hurt.

"It can wait," Jordan said firmly. He was too busy unbuttoning her trousers and touching her in places where no one else had ever dared venture, and she was too hot to make him stop. What had happened with the fire that suddenly she was panting with the warmth that filled the room?

"Wait…" Jordan pulled himself away from her, breathing raggedly as he surveyed the prize that he was about to plunder again.

He strode into the bedroom and returned with the fur blanket.

"What's this?" Chalcie asked, still panting. She stretched like a cat and beckoned him to come to her again, to let their skins meet like silk and sand, rough and smooth against each other.

"I've wanted a repeat performance of making love to you on this fur, on the ground. It stirs up memories."

"And wooden floors will be better than the pine boughs?" She tantalized him, touching him with her fingertips and withdrawing just at the time he moved close, making him groan with anticipation.

"If it isn't just as good, then we'll go back up on the mountains, as soon as it isn't so damned cold, and try it with the pine boughs," Jordan answered. He picked her up and lay down on the fur with her.

If the first time had been wonderful, this time was the best. Together they reached a shattering climax and then relaxed in an embrace.

"Now, what was it you said about having to talk to me?" Jordan said afterward, tracing Chalcie's sweat-laced breast with his fingertips.

Chalcie shivered.

"Are you cold?" Jordan asked with concern.

"No…" Chalcie said. She wasn't cold. She was frightened. If that was the last time she'd hold him close, she'd die. She couldn't face the idea of life without Jordan, but once he knew…

"All right, Chalcie. Tell me the mystery. You've just gone dead white and your eyes lost their laughter, and I'm not going to have you worrying over something that perhaps I can help with," Jordan said quietly.

Chalcie sat up and wrapped herself in one end of the fur blanket. She couldn't stand to have him looking at her naked, revealing everything, when he might throw her out in a few seconds.

"A few days ago—when we'd gone for months without touching and I didn't think you even knew I was alive…" Chalcie gulped and tried to find the courage to continue.

"Yes?" Jordan was eyeing her, and she thought she detected the beginnings of a smile.

"No, it's not funny!"

"I didn't say it was funny," Jordan said, raising his hands defensively.

"Then don't laugh at me. This is awful, Jordan."

"Nothing that the woman I love has done is awful," Jordan said again. He reached for her but she drew away.

"This is. I went to Johnny Tong." There, it was out.

"Were you sick? Is there something wrong?" Jordan sat up, instantly solicitous.

"No, there's nothing wrong. At least nothing wrong with me. But with you…" Chalcie just couldn't go on.

"With me? You went to Mr. Tong about me?" His eyebrows were drawing together and somehow it looked as if he'd lost at least a little bit of his sense of humor.

Chalcie nodded miserably.

"Why?" Jordan barked.

Chalcie's shoulders slumped. "Because I wanted you to love me. I couldn't stand living in the same house with you and not even having you touch me. I thought that if you loved me, everything would be all right, no matter how that love happened.''

Jordan watched her, and the glint was back in his eye.

''Don't you understand?'' Chalcie burst out. ''I went to Johnny Tong and he gave me something to make you love me. You don't really care about me, you never did, not until you ate those damned apple dumplings. And now you'll hate me…'' Chalcie broke down and cried.

Jordan shouted with laughter. He lay back in the fur and rolled back and forth in glee. He guffawed so hard that he had to wipe tears from his eyes. He held his stomach as he roared.

Chalcie looked at him in alarm. Had he suddenly gone mad? No man should have reacted to the idea that his wife had snared him through a love potion by laughing at her. He should have been angry at her. He should have ordered her out of the house for cheating him. And he was laughing? She began to edge away, wondering if dousing him with cold water would bring him back to sanity.

''Jordan?'' she asked tentatively.

Jordan raised his hands and then laughed again. He couldn't even say a word. He was still convulsed at some private joke.

''What is it?'' Chalcie asked again.

This time Jordan managed to bring himself under control enough to speak. ''You took it seriously,'' he said, and his laughter pealed through the house again.

''Took it seriously? Don't you understand? It was one of Mr. Tong's special potions guaranteed to make you love me. And it worked, Jordan. You hadn't even touched me before that night, and then suddenly you were making love to me.'' Not only was Chalcie frightened by his reaction, but she was beginning to be a little bit irritated at him. It wasn't any laughing matter.

''All those months…'' Jordan bit his lip, trying not to make her more angry by laughing again.

Chalcie looked sharply at him. "Why doesn't this bother you? Most men would be furious!"

Jordan took a deep breath and sat up slowly. He still hurt from laughing so hard at Chalcie's confession.

"I'm not mad, because I knew all about it. I thought you knew it was...kind of a joke."

"Joke?" Chalcie's voice was beginning to rise now, but not from any sense of humor. A joke?

"Yeah. Johnny Tong knew exactly who you were. He knew about our marriage, of course. When you came in asking for something that would make me be more, shall we say, receptive to your feminine wiles, he realized that our marriage wasn't all it should have been. Johnny is one smart man, as you may have noticed."

Chalcie frowned. Yes, he was smart. Maybe just a little too smart. "I still don't quite understand the joke, Jordan." Her voice was frosty. "He did give me some herbs to use in the cooking. He said that it would work on you. He promised results."

"I'll bet he did." Jordan started to laugh again, then bit it off. Chalcie was gritting her teeth, and that didn't look like the sign of a woman who was enjoying herself.

"Mr. Tong caught me later that morning as I was coming out of the bar. He told me what he had done, and that he had given you some spices to use on me to make me more virile. He and I are friends, and he has watched us together..."

"Yes?" Chalcie said.

"Well, he knew that I desired you, and he surmised that what was needed was something to make you think I wanted you, and the only prodding that I would need with such a beautiful woman was to make certain I knew that you'd been set up with the spices." Jordan began to laugh again. "You should have seen your face when I said I didn't want the apple dumplings. You looked like you were going to cry!"

"You mean you knew all the time that I'd tried to use

a love potion on you? You knew that Mr. Tong sent that whatever it was home with me?''

"It was ginger and ginseng. Ginseng is what the Chinese use to promote virility, so it wasn't totally useless. But yes, I knew.''

Chalcie was ready to scream. "You let me suffer, thinking that you were only staying with me because of that damned mix of ginger and ginseng instead of loving me for myself?''

Jordan smiled and cocked his head to one side, studying her. "Yes, as a matter of fact, I did let you suffer. You'd made me keep my hands off you when I wanted nothing more than to come out here and ravish you. You made it very clear that it was a marriage of convenience. You didn't even want me in the same room with you. When Tong told me what you'd been in asking for, I wasn't about to let such a wonderful opportunity go past me.''

Chalcie looked at him, her eyes huge and tragic. "But did you ever love me? I thought the potion would make you love me, even if it was a false love.''

Jordan reached over and grabbed her. He pulled the fur blanket from in front of her, and within seconds they were sprawled side by side on the floor. "I think I've always loved you. It just took a while to realize it.''

"Are you sure it wasn't my father's wealth that enticed you?'' Chalcie wasn't absolutely certain of him yet.

"Your father's wealth? Hell, woman, you know I have three times what he had. And incidentally, if you still think I want the Kent holdings, please disabuse yourself of that notion. You can have everything you ever owned in your own name. I don't want it. In fact I told you that months ago. The only thing I want is your love.''

Chalcie smiled up at him, and the impish humor shone in her eyes. "Would you mind terribly, then, if we changed things just a little? I think we need to concentrate on the marriage. And to do that, we need it to be our land, our bars and, to the end, our own true love."

Jordan kissed her. "Our own true love, forever."

*   *   *   *   *

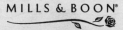

Historical Romance™

THE MASTER OF MOOR HOUSE
by Anne Ashley

The dawn of a new century…

For Megan Drew, the arrival of 1800 brought back Christian Blackmore into her life. Both of them had changed immeasurably, but if Megan were truthful, *one* thing had never changed—her feelings for the man she loved beyond words.

THE QUIET MAN
by Paula Marshall

The dawn of a new century…

For Allen Marriott, 1899 was proving to be a tumultuous time. Not wishing to reveal his connection to his employer, Gerard Schuyler, he was forced to involve Trish Courtney in his secret, heightening the thrill of their illicit meetings…

On sale from 3rd December 1999

Available at most branches of WH Smith, Tesco, Martins, Borders, Easons, Volume One/James Thin and most good paperback bookshops

THE
Regency
COLLECTION

Where rogues find romance

**Look out for the eighth volume in this limited
collection of Regency Romances from
Mills & Boon® in December.**

Featuring:

Fair Juno
by Stephanie Laurens

and

Serafina
by Sylvia Andrew

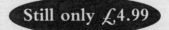

Still only £4.99

MILLS & BOON®

Makes any time special™

FREE!

2 Books
and a surprise gift!

We would like to take this opportunity to thank you for reading this Mills & Boon® book by offering you the chance to take TWO more specially selected titles from the Historical Romance™ series absolutely FREE! We're also making this offer to introduce you to the benefits of the Reader Service™—

- ★ FREE home delivery
- ★ FREE gifts and competitions
- ★ FREE monthly Newsletter
- ★ Books available before they're in the shops
- ★ Exclusive Reader Service discounts

Accepting these FREE books and gift places you under no obligation to buy; you may cancel at any time, even after receiving your free shipment. Simply complete your details below and return the entire page to the address below. *You don't even need a stamp!*

YES! Please send me 2 free Historical Romance books and a surprise gift. I understand that unless you hear from me, I will receive 4 superb new titles every month for just £2.99 each, postage and packing free. I am under no obligation to purchase any books and may cancel my subscription at any time. The free books and gift will be mine to keep in any case.

H9EB

Ms/Mrs/Miss/Mr ....Initials...............................
BLOCK CAPITALS PLEASE

Surname...

Address...

....

....Postcode ....

Send this whole page to:
UK: The Reader Service, FREEPOST CN81, Croydon, CR9 3WZ
EIRE: The Reader Service, PO Box 4546, Kilcock, County Kildare (stamp required)

MILLS & BOON®

MISTLETOE *Magic*

Three favourite Enchanted™ authors
bring you romance at Christmas.

Three stories in one volume:

A Christmas Romance
BETTY NEELS

Outback Christmas
MARGARET WAY

Sarah's First Christmas
REBECCA WINTERS

Published 19th November 1999

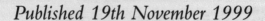